Automotive Test Equipment You Can Build

By

A. Edward Evenson

HOWARD W. SAMS & CO., INC.
THE BOBBS-MERRILL CO., INC.
INDIANAPOLIS • KANSAS CITY • NEW YORK

FIRST EDITION

FIRST PRINTING—1972

International Standard Book Number: 0-672-20926-8
Library of Congress Catalog Card Number: 72-84434

Preface

Every year, more and more car owners are servicing their own vehicles. For some, it is simply a matter of economics—for others, a fascinating hobby. Regardless of the reason, one soon finds that he can go only so far without special equipment. The question that arises, however, is: How far can I go before the cost of the instruments exceeds the savings of doing my own work? Naturally, you can do a great deal of troubleshooting and servicing with the highly effective—but costly—professional level equipment. But to spend a hundred dollars or more to save twenty dollars defeats the purpose. On the other hand, the lower priced, do-it-yourself type instruments are usually limited in what they can do.

The only economical answer is to build your own "professional level" instruments. The purpose of this book is to assist you in doing so. Realizing that not everyone has the same specific interests in automotive servicing, I have tried to cover a variety of instruments from simple, single purpose testers to mutlifunction analyzers. The builder has considerable flexibility as to which test circuits or combinations he selects. To assure reliability, all circuits are based on proven commercial designs.

Each chapter describes a particular test instrument, covering not only construction and theory of operation, but applications and testing procedures as well. Whether your primary inclination is toward electricity or toward mechanics, you will have no difficulty in building your own equipment. No specialized skill or electronic knowledge is needed. And of course, there is a great deal of satisfaction in being able to troubleshoot and tune your own car with your own custom-made instruments.

A. EDWARD EVENSON

Contents

Introduction

This book is somewhat different from most project-type books. It incorporates a modular or building block approach: the first seven chapters discuss separate projects that can be combined into a comprehensive yet easily built automotive analyzer, described in Chapter 8. It is suggested that you read this chapter first. The building-block structure of this book allows you to tailor the analyzer to fit your particular requirements. You may be as plain or fancy as you wish.

Each of the first seven chapters describes a separate test instrument built around its own printed-circuit board. These can be used either separately or combined with others in the multifunction analyzer. For example, you may begin building toward the analyzer with only a dwellmeter (Chapter 1) and then later add a tachometer (Chapter 2). Depending on your needs and pocketbook, you may add other test functions—such as an ignition tester (Chapter 4) or an alternator tester (Chapter 7)—until eventually you have a complete automotive analyzer.

Your analyzer can have a professional appearance if you utilize the full-size layouts provided in this book. Included are layouts for the panel, meter dial, and printed-circuit boards. These can be copied as shown or serve as guides for your own creative designs. Many of the other projects also include meter dial layouts.

Before beginning any actual construction, it is also suggested that you read Chapter 15. It discusses parts selection and construction techniques. You have a certain amount of freedom in choosing the parts you use and the methods of construction, both of which influence the cost of the completed instruments. Every attempt has been made to keep construction costs low without sacrificing performance. For example, all meter circuits use the economical 0–1 milliampere meter movement.

The rest of the book describes various supplementary test instruments such as timing lights coil testers, battery testers and other projects. For those who would like to experiment with automotive oscilloscope testing, a chapter has been devoted to this subject. It shows how to adapt a standard oscilloscope for this purpose and how to analyze the various waveforms.

With the projects covered in this book you can successfully diagnose and service the complete electrical and ignition systems of automobiles as well as assure factory specified tune-up requirements.

1

The Dwellmeter

The terms dwell, dwell angle, and cam angle mean the same thing. They refer to the duration of closure of the ignition breaker points, and the dwellmeter, of course, is the instrument used to measure this duration. The purpose of this chapter is to show how a dwellmeter works, how to build one, and how to use it.

Although the functioning of the points and the importance of their adjustment are generally known, certain aspects should be considered to understand better the operation of the dwellmeter. Let us review briefly the ignition process.

As shown in Fig. 1-1 the breaker points are made to open and close by a cam (called the distributor cam) rotating at half the speed of the engine. The cam allows the points to remain in contact for a certain period of time and then separates them at the proper instant. The spark occurs at the time of separation.

The closed portion is called the "dwell period." There is no specific name for the open period. During the dwell period, current flows through the coil primary winding. Because the coil is inductive, it takes time for this current to build up to its maximum value (Fig. 1-2). When the points open, the amount of primary current determines the coil output; the more current at break, the higher the output. Therefore, it is desirable to have a relatively long dwell period, especially at higher speeds where there is little time for coil current to build up. However, if the dwell period is too long, point separation will not be ample to prevent arc-over. This condition lowers coil output.

Dwell specifications, as given by the car manufacturers, provide not only for sufficient coil current buildup and adequate point opening, but also establish the proper rotor-cap relationship. When the points separate to cause the ignition spark, the rotor should be adja-

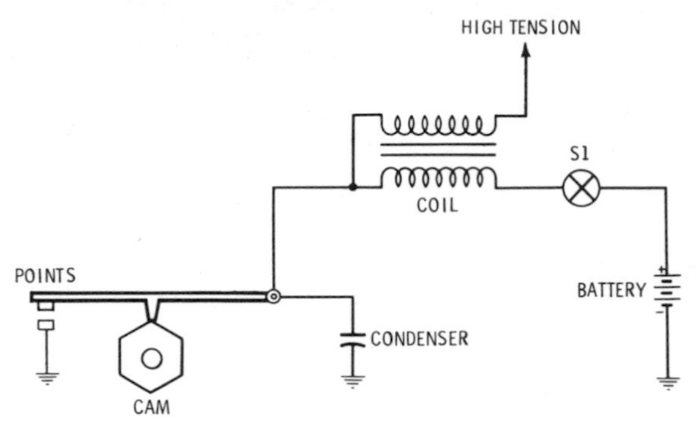

Fig. 1-1. Basic ignition system.

cent to one of the cap segments. Improper dwell, either too much or too little, affects this relationship, causing the rotor to be behind or ahead of its proper position.

In earlier years, dwell was specified in terms of the breaker point gap. There is a definite relationship between maximum point separation (gap) and dwell angle; if you set one, you automatically get the other (Fig. 1-3). Today, with the widespread use of dwellmeters, most car manufacturers give both gap and dwell specifications. The dwell method, of course, is the easiest and most accurate way of adjusting points.

There are actually two ways of specifying dwell angle: the degree of dwell method and the percent of dwell method. Both methods are found in Europe, but the degree method is primarily American. First, consider the degree of dwell method which refers to the number of degrees of distributor cam rotation that the contact points remain closed. For example, a 6-cylinder engine has a six-lobe distributor cam. This means that 60° (360°/6) of cam rotation will be allotted to the ignition cycle for each cylinder. Of this 60°, a portion is for the points closed or dwell period and the remainder for the points open

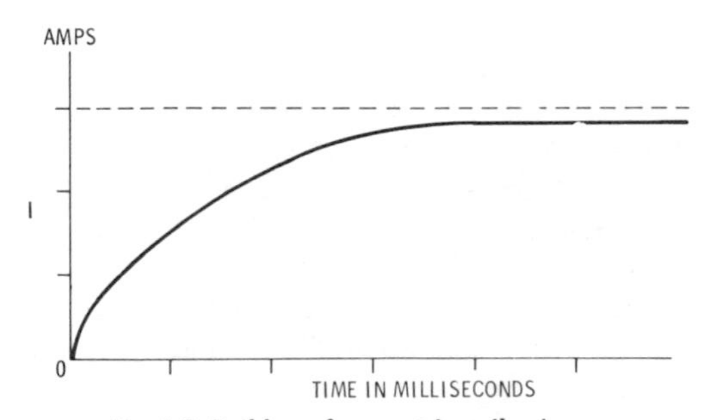

Fig. 1-2. Buildup of current in coil primary.

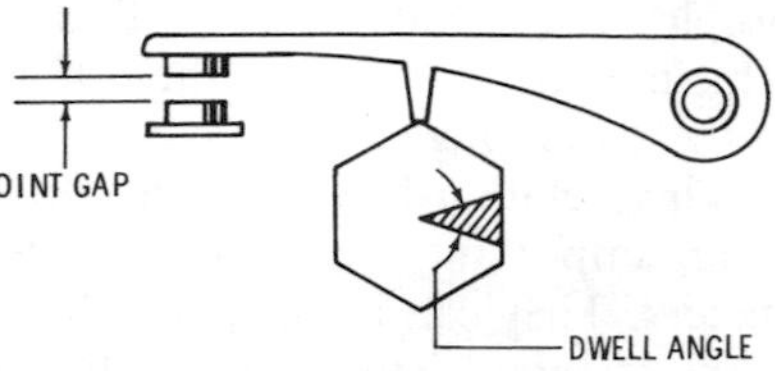

POINT GAP

DWELL ANGLE

Fig. 1-3. Relationship of point dwell to point gap.

period. A typical 6-cylinder dwell specification might be 36°. In other words, the points will remain closed for 36° and open for 24°. This cycle repeats as each cylinder is fired.

In an 8-cylinder engine there are only 45° (360°/8) allotted to each cylinder. An 8-cylinder dwell specification can never exceed 45°. In fact, at 45° of dwell the points would remain permanently closed and there would be no ignition. Eight-cylinder engine dwell angles are generally in a range from 28° to 32°. However, by overlapping two smaller dwell periods, dwell angles up to 42° are possible with dual points. The technique for adjusting dual points is covered at the end of this chapter.

Following the above reasoning, we see that 4-cylinder engines have a maximum dwell of 90°. However, the typical range may vary considerably—from a low of about 30° to over 75°. As you can see, the degree of dwell method depends on the number of cylinders, or more specifically, the number of lobes on the distributor cam (Fig. 1-4). In most cases, the number of lobes equals the number of cylinders, but occasionally you may find an 8-cylinder engine employing dual ignition with two separate but staggered ignition systems operated by a common four-lobe cam. The individual dwell angles, in this case, would be treated as two separate 4-cylinder ignition systems. Outboard motors sometimes use dual ignition, also.

With the percent-of-dwell method, it is not necessary to know the number of cylinders or cam lobes. The percent of dwell merely states what percentage of time the points remain closed. There is a simple relationship between percent of dwell and degrees of dwell. For ex-

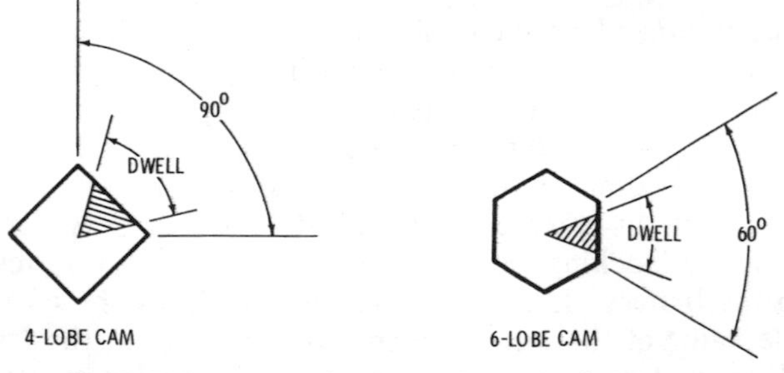

Fig. 1-4. Comparing dwell period to cam design.

ample, the dwell of a 6-cylinder engine might be given as 60%. This means that 60% of the 60° is allotted to each cam lobe, or, 36° is the dwell angle.

This relationship between percent of dwell and degrees of dwell is an important one. All dwellmeters are basically percent-of-dwell meters. They can be made to show degrees of dwell (Fig. 1-5), which is the standard American practice, in two ways: (1) by drawing separate scales for each number of cylinders or (2) by using one scale and adjusting meter current in accord with the number of cylinders.

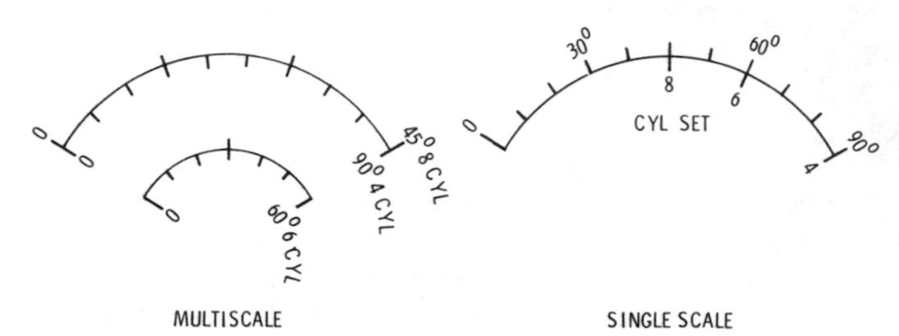

Fig. 1-5. Various dwell scales.

HOW DWELLMETERS WORK

There are two circuits commonly used for measuring dwell: the externally powered circuit and the internally powered circuit. The externally powered circuit has the advantage of not requiring any internal batteries. It is also quite simple to build. This is the type used in the Mini-Analyzer, described in detail in Chapter 10.

The internally powered circuit has the advantage of being somewhat more accurate than the above circuit, especially at higher speeds. This is the type of circuit generally found in more expensive equipment. It is basically a switching circuit that turns meter current on when the points are closed, and off when they open. The switching can be accomplished either by transistors or diodes, both ways being commonly used. The dwell circuit shown here is the diode switching type.

The operation of an internally powered dwell circuit can be seen by considering the basic circuit shown in Fig. 1-6. Some of the early dwellmeters were made in this manner. The input is connected directly across the points. Dwellmeters sense the opening and closing of the points by responding to the voltage appearing across them.

When the points close, current from the tester battery flows through the meter, the blocking diode, the points, the calibration resistor, and back to the battery. The calibration resistor limits the current to the full-scale value of the meter. When the points open, the ignition system voltage appears across them. This voltage, being greater than the

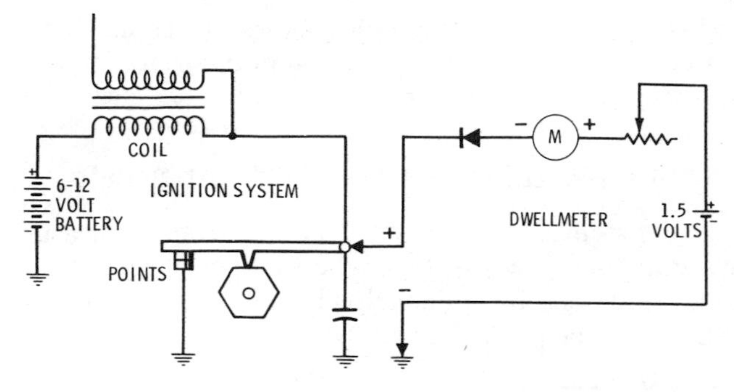

Fig. 1-6. Basic dwell circuit.

dwell circuit voltage, attempts to cause current flow through the meter in a reverse direction. It is blocked by the diode, and meter current during this time is zero.

As the points alternately open and close, the meter receives, alternately, either full-scale current or zero current. The average meter current is proportional to the percentage of time the points are closed. If they are closed 60% of the time, the meter deflection will be 60% of full scale. We need draw only a 0–100 scale to be able to read percent of dwell. We could also draw, for instance, a 0–60 scale and read the degrees of dwell for a 6-cylinder engine.

This basic circuit would work reasonably well at low speeds, but would need some refinements to make it a practical dwellmeter. One problem is that the ignition voltage seen by the dwellmeter is not an ideal rectangular waveform. Rather, it looks like that shown in Fig. 1-7. The particular shape varies with speed and ignition load. (This will be discussed in more detail in Chapter 12.) The dwellmeter should be relatively immune to these variations, since they have no effect on the actual dwell.

Another problem is caused by the point contact resistance. Even when closed, the points can still develop a slight voltage that can affect a dwellmeter. Chapter 3 describes an instrument specifically designed to measure this voltage. It is the prime indicator of point

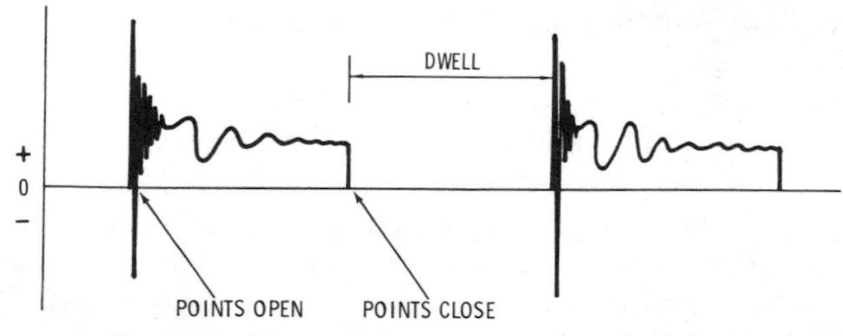

Fig. 1-7. Ignition waveform as seen across the points.

quality. However, this voltage which amounts to as much as 10% of the effective dwell circuit voltage does nothing to improve dwellmeter accuracy. Better dwell circuits reject this voltage.

THE DWELLMETER PRINTED-CIRCUIT BOARD

Here is a practical dwell circuit that accurately measures dwell from slow cranking speeds to the highest engine speeds. It is virtually immune to variations in ignition load and breaker point resistance and works on either 6- or 12-volt systems.

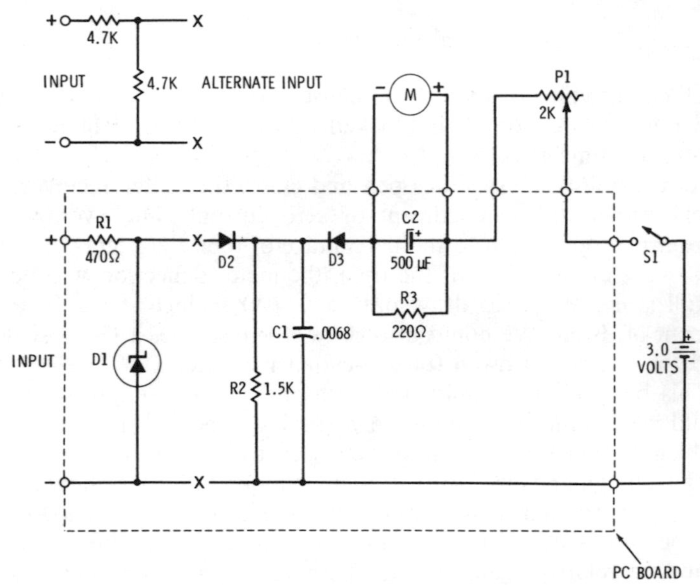

Fig. 1-8. Schematic of dwell printed-circuit board.

There are two parts to the circuit: the input regulator and the actual dwell circuit. The input regulator (R1 and D1) shapes the ignition waveform which appears across the points into a rough rectangular form before it is applied to the dwell circuit. At a slight sacrifice in high-speed performance, the input regulator can be replaced with the alternate voltage divider shown in Fig. 1-8.

The circuit works in this manner. When the points close, current from the 3-volt battery flows through the calibration control, the meter, diode D3, load R2, and back to the battery. Diode D2 prevents this current from flowing through the points. Also, this current developes a voltage across R2. As long as the voltage across the points (due to contact resistance) is less than the voltage across R2, it will have no effect on the meter reading.

Table 1-1. Parts List for Dwellmeter

Item	Description
C1	Capacitor, .0068 μF, 200 Volts
C2	Capacitor, 500 μF, 3–6 volts, electrolytic
D1	Diode, zener, 5.1 volts, 1 watt
D2, D3	Diode, silicon, 200 piv
M	Meter, 0–1 mA, 50-ohms internal resistance
P1	Rheostat, 2K
R1	Resistor, 470 ohms, 1 watt, 10%
R2	Resistor, 1.5K, ½ watt, 10%
R3	Resistor, 220 ohms, ½ watt, 10%
S1	Switch, toggle, spst

When the points open, the ignition voltage across them is much greater than the dwell circuit voltage. The ignition voltage is clamped at about 5 volts by the zener, passes through D2, and appears across R2. This voltage across R2, being greater than the meter circuit voltage, effectively blocks the meter current by the action of D3. The meter response is the same as previously described.

The large capacitor across the meter is used for damping and thereby provides a steady meter reading at slow cranking speeds. This is a definite advantage when installing or adjusting points. See Table 1-1 for the dwellmeter parts list.

CONSTRUCTION NOTES

A full-size, printed-circuit pattern for the module is shown in Fig. 1-9. This can be reproduced photographically (only a negative is required) if you plan to make the board with the photo-resist method. If not, you can simply trace the pattern onto the copper, using carbon

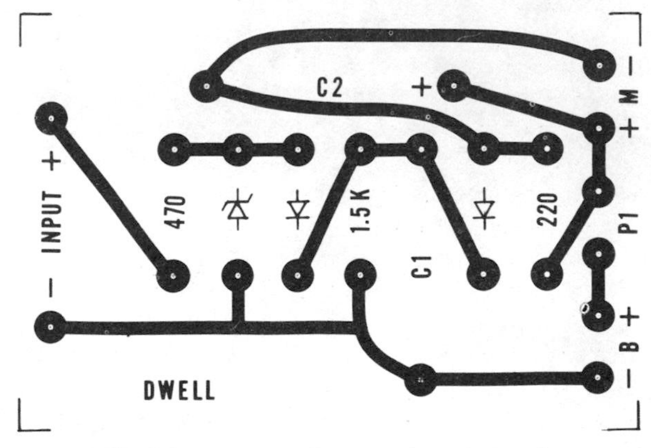

Fig. 1-9. PC pattern for printed-circuit board.

paper, and fill in the pattern with resist. Etch in the normal manner and remove the resist.

There are no critical parts in the circuit; 10%-tolerance components are adequate. Because it functions only as a clamp, the zener diode need not be an expensive type. The voltage source consists of two 1.5-volt batteries.

The completed printed-circuit board (Fig. 1-10) can be used either in a single-purpose (dwellmeter only) instrument or incorporated into the Master Analyzer as described in Chapter 8.

If the printed-circuit board is to be used in the Master Analyzer described in Chapter 8, change the 1.5K resistor to 2.7K, and connect a jumper between the P1 terminals on the board. This change compensates for the change in battery voltage. The Master Analyzer uses a 4.5-volt battery source, with a common adjusting control for both the dwellmeter and the tachometer.

As mentioned earlier, there are several ways in which a dwellmeter can be calibrated, depending on the scale layout. A practical arrangement is shown in Fig. 1-11. In this arrangement, 6- and 8-cylinder dwells are read on the 0–60° scale and 4-cylinder dwells are read on the 0–90° scale.

The dwell calibration control is mounted on the instrument panel so as to be accessible to the operator. Before connecting the instru-

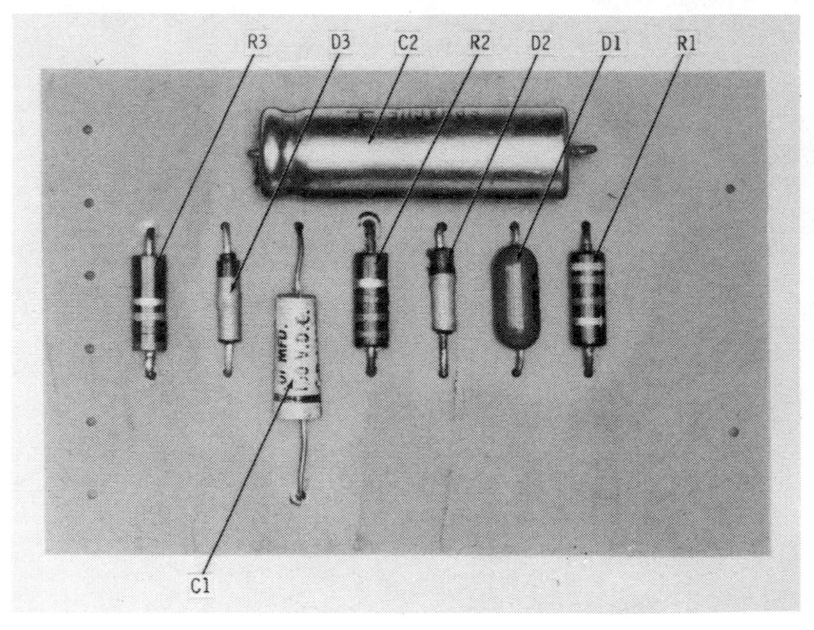

Fig. 1-10. Completed printed-circuit board.

ment to an engine, this control is adjusted to give a meter reading of 45°, 60°, or 90°, depending on the number of cylinders. Be sure, however, to do this on the proper scale.

The completed instrument can be checked as follows. After calibrating to full scale, connect the input to a variable voltage source. The meter should remain at full scale as the input voltage is increased from zero to about 2 volts. Before 5 volts is reached, the meter should return to zero. The meter should remain at zero from 5 volts to 15 volts. If these conditions are not met, recheck the component values, including the diodes.

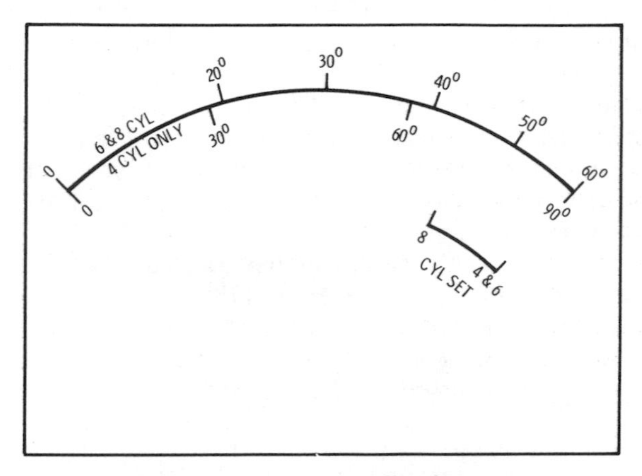

Fig. 1-11. Dwell scales.

HOW TO USE THE DWELLMETER

Be sure the dwellmeter is calibrated, as described above, prior to each use. Because practically all cars today have a negative ground, connect the test leads as follows: positive to the distributor primary terminal (either on the distributor or the coil) and negative to engine ground (Fig. 1-12). Reverse these connections if you have a car with a positive ground.

There are two tests normally made with a dwellmeter: (1) the idle dwell test and (2) the dwell variation test. The first is made by noting the dwell reading with the engine at normal idle speed. The reading should be within the manufacturer's recommended range. This test will be discussed again later.

The dwell variation test requires the measurement of the amount of dwell variation as engine speed is increased from idle to about 2000 rpm. Its purpose is to detect wear in the distributor. However, the test can be misleading if you do not understand the difference between the two basic types of distributors.

In most distributors, the points are mounted on a movable plate (the breaker plate) so the timing can be advanced in accord with engine load. This is accomplished by a vacuum control attached to the breaker plate and actuated by engine manifold vacuum which is proportional to engine load.

In the concentric type, the breaker plate moves concentrically with the distributor cam. Because there is no change in the relative position of the points, even during advance and retard, the dwell should not change by more than 2°. If a greater change is noted, it indicates a defective breaker plate or possibly a worn distributor shaft. The plate can be made stationary by disconnecting the vacuum line. If a repeat test shows no change, you can be quite certain the breaker plate is defective.

In eccentric type the breaker plate moves across the cam. This will normally cause a change in dwell reading as engine speed changes. The car manufacturer specifies this change which varies from 3° to about 8°. If no change is noted, the breaker plate or vacuum advance control is defective.

One of the greatest advantages of the dwellmeter is in setting or adjusting the points. If you have ever used the old feeler-gauge method of adjustment, you will appreciate the dwellmeter. It's not only more accurate, but easier and quicker. Some distributors have a small window through which the dwell can be adjusted while the engine is running. With all other distributors, this must be done with the engine cranking and the cap removed.

When the dwell is set by cranking, the plugs should be removed. This puts the least strain on the battery. However, it can be done with the plugs in if you do not crank the engine more than 20 or 30 seconds at a time.

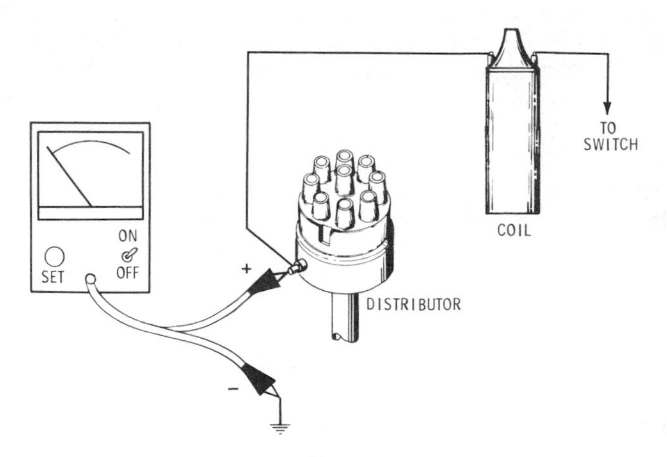

Fig. 1-12. Connecting the dwellmeter.

Before setting dwell, remove the high-tension wire from the center of the cap and ground it. This keeps the sparks from jumping. Remove the cap and rotor. Loosen the screw holding the points just enough so the points can move. Connect the dwellmeter and turn on the ignition. While the engine is cranking, adjust the points to the specified amount. Recheck the dwell after tightening the point locking screw as sometimes the dwell will change slightly.

Dwell is frequently given as a range; for example, 28° to 32°. Any setting in this range is acceptable. But generally, it is set to the low end to allow for the normal rubbing block wear that causes dwell to increase. Even after considerable wear, the dwell will still be in tolerance.

Some distributors have dual points. These are adjusted in the same manner, but with one exception. One set of points is blocked open, while the other set is being adjusted. When both sets have been individually adjusted, remove the block and check the overall or combined dwell.

The idle dwell test mentioned earlier is a simple test which indicates the need to retime your engine. This is how it works. After properly timing the engine with a power timing light (or other specified means), note and record the idle dwell reading. As long as the idle dwell remains the same during periodic checks, the timing remains the same. This assumes, of course, that the engine has not been retimed in the interim.

Wear of the rubbing block causes the dwell to increase. This condition, in turn causes the timing to become retarded. The relationship is that for every one-degree change in dwell, there is a corresponding one-degree change in timing. Resetting the dwell to its original setting will restore the original timing. This holds true for single breaker systems only. With dual points the situation is more difficult, since only the break set of points (not the make set) controls the timing.

Whenever new points are installed, the engine should always be retimed as specified. And always remember the cardinal rule. Dwell affects timing. Adjust dwell before setting timing.

2

The Tachometer

The tachometer is perhaps the most popular and widely used of all automotive test instruments. Because it is almost basic to testing and tune-up, it is usually one of the first metered instruments acquired by the home mechanic. In fact, it would be difficult to do a good tune-up without one. They are also valuable companion instruments to many other automotive testers, as we shall see in the following chapters.

Tachometers have always been fascinating construction projects. For this reason, one purpose of this chapter will be to give some general guidelines for devising various "tach" circuits to suit different requirements. In addition, we will show how to make a test tach that can be used either as a separate instrument or combined with other test circuits, as in the Master Analyzer of Chapter 8.

HOW A TACHOMETER WORKS

A wide variety of tachs have been developed over the years. Their operation may be mechanical, magnetic, electrical, or some combinational arrangement. The electrical impulse tach is the type most frequently used for automotive test purposes and the type best suited to home construction. It is called an impulse tach because it counts impulses, not revolutions. However, because there is a fixed relationship between the impulses counted and the speed of the engine producing them, the meter can be scaled directly in rpm (revolutions per minute).

The impulses created by the ignition system, especially those generated by the opening and closing of the breaker points, can be used to power a tach circuit directly (see Chapter 10) or merely as a trigger for a tach circuit. This latter approach is used with the so-called transistorized tachs and will be the one used in this chapter.

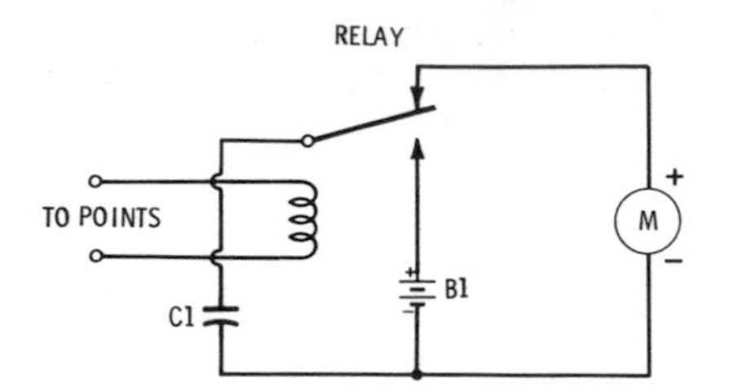

Fig. 2-1. Relay operated tachometer.

A tach circuit, regardless of its mode of operation, is basically a pulse generator. Its function is to generate constant energy pulses that will be applied to an indicating meter. The circuit produces one constant energy pulse each time it receives one of the above-mentioned triggering impulses. The more pulses applied to the meter in a given period of time, the greater will be its deflection. In other words, the average meter current depends on the repetition rate of the pulses. One method of generating constant energy pulses is shown in Fig. 2-1.

Fig. 2-1 is typical of the early relay tachs used for automotive purposes. It performs the same function as a modern transistorized tach which is to generate and feed constant energy pulses into a meter. Its simple circuit shows the functioning of an impulse tach.

The driving coil of the relay is connected directly across the ignition breaker points. The relay armature follows their action. When the points open and energize the relay, the armature moves to the lower contact. This allows the capacitor to charge quickly to the level of the fixed voltage source. When the points close and de-energize the relay, the armature moves to the upper contact. The capacitor now discharges through the meter causing a momentary upscale deflection of the pointer. This process repeats itself each time the points open and close. As a result, the meter receives an average current dependent on the repetition rate and energy content of the pulses. Because the voltage source and condenser capacitance remain fixed, pulse energy is constant. The only variable is pulse repetition rate, which is proportional to engine speed.

A similar circuit function can be obtained by substituting a simple transistor switch for the relay. This is a common approach. Notice the similarity between the transistorized circuit of Fig. 2-2 and the previous relay circuit. When the transistor is nonconducting (no input signal), the capacitor charges from the fixed voltage of the battery through R1 and D1. The charging current is prevented from passing through the meter by the blocking action of D2.

When the points open, the ignition voltage, after being filtered by the input circuit, appears at the transistor base and drives it into saturation. The previously charged capacitor now appears connected across the meter and diode D2. The polarity of the charge on the capacitor is such that it will discharge through D2 and the meter causing an upscale deflection. It cannot discharge through D1. As far as the *meter* is concerned, the circuit action is the same as with the relay method.

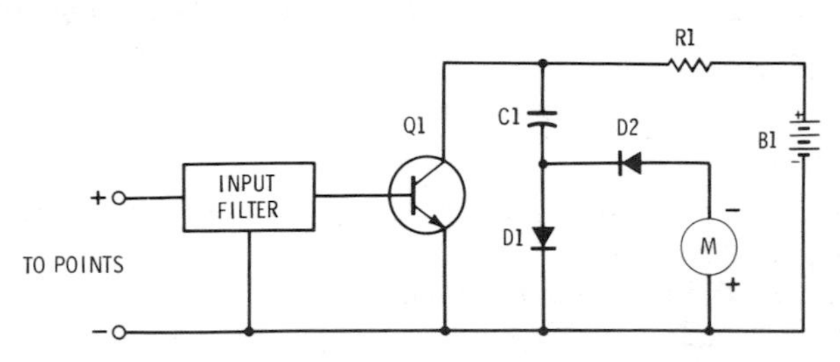

Fig. 2-2. Transistorized tachometer.

DETERMINING TACHOMETER RANGES

For those who might like to experiment with tachs, there is a simple relationship between circuit values and scale range. To show this, consider the tach not as an rpm meter, but as an impulse counter. It counts each impulse generated by the ignition system—one impulse per plug firing. First, convert engine rpm into impulses per second. Assume that you require a tach reading from 0 to 1200 rpm on a 6-cylinder engine. The maximum impulses per second (IPS) to be measured is determined by the following formula:

$$\text{IPS} = \frac{\text{Maximum scale rpm} \times \text{No. of cylinders}}{120}$$

$$= \frac{1200 \times 6}{120}$$

$$= 60 \text{ IPS}$$

This formula is for four-cycle engines, in which the distributor turns at half engine speed. This, of course, applies to virtually all automotive engines. For two-cycle engines, divide by 60 instead of 120.

Now that you have the maximum IPS to be measured, use the following formula to determine the circuit values. It will be apparent that you have a variety of combinations that will give the desired results.

$$I = F \times E \times C$$

where,

I is the full-scale meter current in microamps,
F is the maximum impulses per second,
E is the circuit voltage,
C is the condenser capacity in microfarads.

Normally, you will be working with a given meter sensitivity and circuit voltage. This reduces the problem merely to finding the correct condenser capacitance. Continuing with our original example, let's assume that you have a 0–1 mA (or 0–1000 μA) meter and a 3-volt battery. Putting these values into the formula and solving for C, we have:

$$1000 = 60 \times 3 \times C$$

or

$$C = 5.55\ \mu F$$

If you used these values in a relay tach, the meter would register full scale at exactly 1200 rpm on a 6-cylinder engine. In a transistorized circuit you might be as much as 2 to 3% below full scale. This is due to the imperfect switching action of diodes with slight inverse leakage. However, this is of little concern because the usual practice is to select a capacitor approximately 15% over the calculated value. The excess meter current can be bypassed by shunting a variable resistor across the meter terminals. Calibration of the circuit will be discussed later.

TIME CONSTANTS

Be careful in the selection of resistor values for the capacitor charging and discharging circuits. This includes collector load and meter resistances. These resistances form RC time constant circuits with the charging capacitor. If these time constants are too great, the capacitor will not completely charge nor discharge in the interval between ignition impulses. This causes the meter response to be nonlinear, or crowded near the end of the scale range. To avoid this condition the rule is to keep circuit resistance as low as possible, consistent with transistor ratings, or to use a higher voltage source. In practice, the calculated time constants should be ¼ or less of the interval for charging or discharging at the highest rpm. This will provide an essentially linear scale.

The time constant of a resistor-capacitor combination is shown by the simple relationship:

$$T = R \times C$$

where,

T is the time in milliseconds,
R is the resistance in kilohms,
C is the capacitance in microfarads.

In our original example of a 1200-rpm tach for a 6-cylinder engine, we found that we needed a 5.55-μF charge capacitor. Let's see what would happen if a collector load resistor (R1) of 330 ohms were used. See Fig. 2-2. Because the circuit must count a maximum of 60 impulses per second, there will be a minimum of $\frac{1}{60}$ of a second between impulses (.0167 seconds, or approximately 17 milliseconds). Assume that half of this time, or about 8 milliseconds, is allotted to the charging of the capacitor through R1. (The remainder, of course, is for the discharge through the meter.) The time constant of this circuit is 5.55 μF times 330 ohms, or approximately 1.8 milliseconds. Because this is less than ¼ of the allotted 8 milliseconds, we will have a linear circuit. Actually, it will be linear within about 1%, which in most cases is better than the linearity of the meter.

It will be apparent to many readers that there are various ways of generating constant energy pulses other than by the simple transistor switch just described. Specially designed transformers are one means, multivibrators another, and one additional method will be shown in Chapter 10.

BUILDING A TEST TACHOMETER

Having explored the basic elements of tachometer design, let's look at an actual dual-range test tach circuit. This is the circuit project for this chapter. It can be built either as a single function instrument or incorporated into the Master Analyzer described in Chapter 8. The ranges selected are those most common in automotive test tachs. However, by using the previous rules, they can be modified to suit your own particular needs.

The transistor type is not critical as long as it is similar to the one specified. The circuit is designed to work at the 3.8-volt level. This value is based on the useful voltage of three "D" cells less the allowance for battery aging. A calibrating control will correct for loss of battery voltage down to this level. Use capacitors of the value and tolerance specified.

Since we have already discussed the pulse generating portion of the tach, let's consider the input circuit. The purpose of this circuit is to process the ignition waveform that appears across the open points, into a pulse that will drive the transistor into saturation and *hold* it there until the points close. When they do close, input voltage is removed and the transistor reverts to its cutoff state. Switching between saturation and cutoff is necessary to ensure linear circuit response. The circuit details are shown in Fig. 2-3.

The input circuit must also serve another function. When the tach is used on "pointless" transistorized or electronic ignition systems, it must be connected across the ignition switching transistor. When this transistor is on (which is equivalent to the points-closed state of a conventional system), it can develop over half a volt. If the input circuit does not reject this voltage, it could partially turn on the tach transistor, causing inaccuracies. In the above circuit, this voltage is reduced by the components in the input circuit to a value below the conduction level of Q1.

The dual-range feature is accomplished by changing the value of the tach charge capacitor. A review of the previous circuit design formula will show why this is true. In the high range, only capacitor C2 is in the circuit. In the low range, capacitor C3 is connected in parallel with C2. This has the effect of increasing circuit capacitance by a factor of five and giving a five-to-one ratio between the low and high ranges. Notice that capacitor C3 is only *four* times as large as C2. C3 is *added* to C2 in the low-range position.

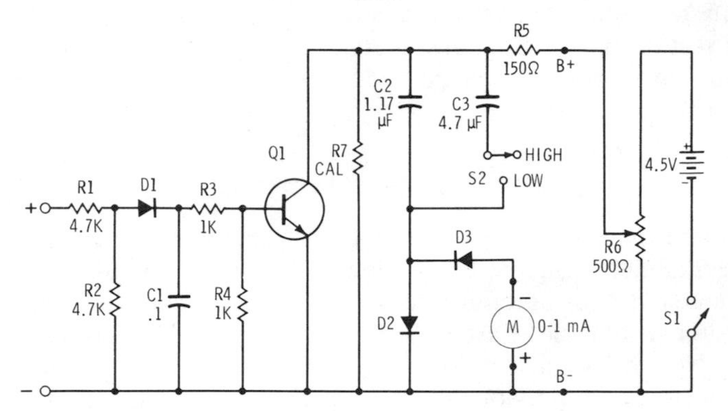

Fig. 2-3. Dual-range test tachometer.

In practice, it is difficult to buy a pair of capacitors, one of which is exactly four times the capacitance of the other. The solution is to "pad" one of the capacitors by paralleling a small value capacitor across it until it is one fourth or four times the value of the other. If you do not have a capacitance measuring instrument, padding can be done as explained later.

If you use the printed-circuit board pattern of Fig. 2-4, circuit construction is quite simple. Be sure to install the diodes in proper polarity. The one next to C1 is a silicon diode; the other two are germanium. Also, be sure to observe the polarity on capacitors C2 and C3. When you trim the leads after soldering, let those of C2 extend about a quarter of an inch from the board. This makes it easy to attach the padder capacitor during calibration. The space marked "cal" is for the circuit calibration resistor. See Table 2-1 for the tachometer parts list.

Upon completion, the circuit board (Fig. 2-5) can be used in a single-function instrument (tach only) or incorporated into the Master Analyzer of Chapter 8. This decision will affect the final wiring and

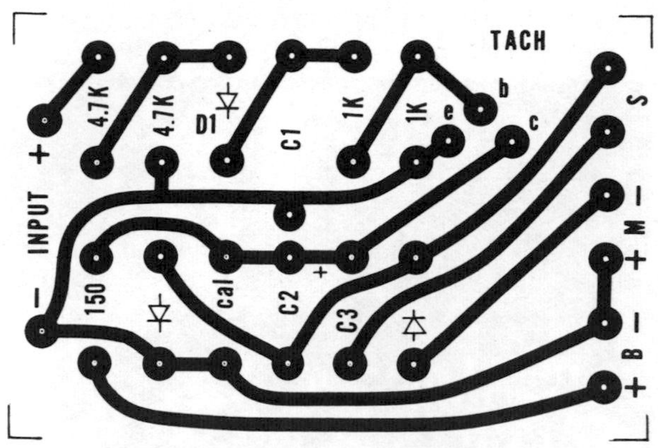

Fig. 2-4. Full-size printed-circuit pattern.

Table 2-1. Parts List for Tachometer

Item	Description
C1	Capacitor, .10 µF, 100 volts
C2	Capacitor, 1.0 µF, 10 volts, tantalum (see text)
C3	Capacitor, 4.7 µF, 10 volts, tantalum
D1	Diode, silicon, 200 volts
D2, D3	Diode, germanium, Type 1N34 or equivalent
M	Meter, 0–1 mA, 50-ohms internal resistance
R1, R2	Resistor, 4.7K, ½ watt, 10%
R3, R4	Resistor, 1K, ½ watt, 10%
R5	Resistor, 150 ohms, ½ watt, 10%
R6	Potentiometer, 500 ohms, wirewound (set control) see Chapter 8
R7	See text
R8*	Rheostat, 5K
Q1	Transistor, 2N1302 or equivalent
S1	Switch, toggle, spst
S2	Switch, toggle, spdt
S3*	Switch, rotary, 3 pole, 3 position

*Additional parts for single-function tachometer (Fig. 2-7).

calibration of the unit. If you add it to the Master Analyzer, it will share the battery power supply with the dwellmeter. Let's consider this method first.

CALIBRATING THE TACHOMETER

When the tach circuit is used in conjunction with the dwellmeter, the tach is automatically calibrated by the dwellmeter. See Chapter 8. It works in this manner. The dwellmeter is calibrated, prior to use, by adjusting the battery or source voltage to give either a 45° or 60° reading on the meter, depending on whether an 8- or 6-cylinder

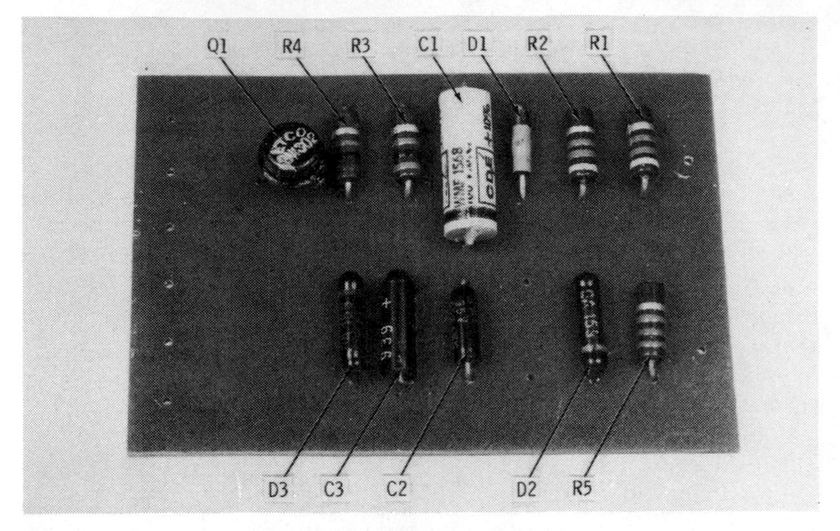

Fig. 2-5. Completed circuit board.

engine is being tested. This sets the source voltage at one of two levels, the ratio of which is 6 to 8. This is also the ratio of the impulses generated by a 6- and 8-cylinder engine operating at the same speed. Therefore, when the dwellmeter is properly set, the voltage supplied to the tach will also be in the proper ratio for either 6- or 8-cylinder engines.

In addition, the tach circuit must be adjusted to produce the same rpm reading for both the LOW and HIGH ranges. This is accomplished by adding a small capacitor (selected experimentally) in parallel with C2. This step should be done first. To do this, use the calibration circuit shown in Fig. 2-6.

With the tach printed-circuit board wired to the analyzer as shown in Chapter 8, connect the test leads to the calibrator of Fig. 2-6. Set the range switch to the LOW position and adjust the battery source R6 (the T-D set control) to give a 1000-rpm reading on the low scale. Then, switch to the HIGH position. If C2 and C3 are properly matched, you will get a 1000-rpm reading on the high scale. Most likely, it will

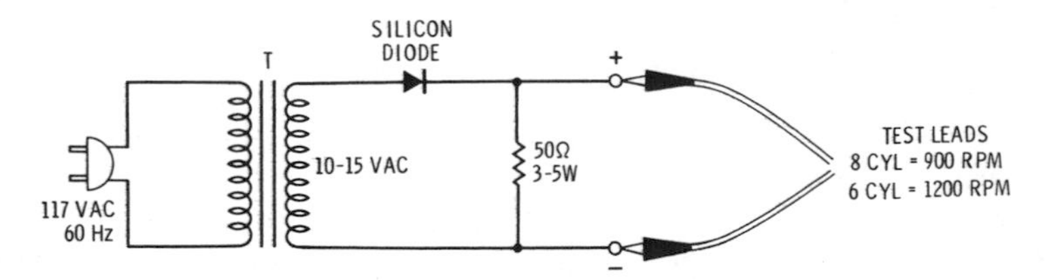

Fig. 2-6. Tachometer calibrator.

be less than this. If so, add a small value capacitor (temporarily clipped in with jumper leads) across C2 and repeat the procedure. Start with about a .05-μF padder. When you obtain the same reading on both scales, C2 and C3 are matched. Solder the padding capacitor to C2. (Note: If, because of capacitor tolerance, C3 is undersize, you must do the padding on C3.)

The next step completes the calibration. Disconnect the test leads from the calibrator and turn to the DWELL position. Adjust the battery source R6 (the T-D Set control) for a 45-degree dwell reading, or, in other words, an 8-cylinder setting. Turn to the LOW tach range. Connect the test leads to the calibrator and note the meter reading. If you read 900 rpm on the low scale, no further calibration is needed. Normally, though, you will be reading over 900 rpm. If so, add resistor R7 (selected experimentally) to the "cal" terminals on the circuit board. Start with about 1.5K and increase or decrease as required to give a 900-rpm reading.

Less than 900 rpm indicates either circuit problems or off-value components. If there are no circuit defects, an under-900-rpm reading is caused by either low circuit voltage or under-capacitance components C2 and C3. Low circuit voltage may be due to the 2.7K dwell circuit resistor being under tolerance. Increase its value by about 270 ohms. If C2 and C3 are under capacitance, add a .2-μF capacitor across C2 and rematch C3. Either or both of these methods may be used to effect tach calibration.

The tach is now calibrated for 6- or 8-cylinder engines on either the HIGH or LOW ranges. To test 4-cylinder engines, set the instrument for 8-cylinder engines and double all tach and dwell readings.

A SINGLE-FUNCTION INSTRUMENT

If you plan to use the printed-circuit board in a "tach only" instrument, a slightly different circuit arrangement is used. (See Fig. 2-7.) Notice that R8 must be added to the circuit. This is an internal control replacing the "cal" resistor. R6 is the front panel SET control. Although any combination of scale ranges can be chosen, a practical arrangement is 0–1200 rpm for the low scale and 0–6000 rpm for the high scale. This keeps the ratio between C2 and C3 the same as previously described, and they are matched in exactly the same way.

After matching C2 and C3, set the instrument to the LOW range and connect the test leads to the calibrator. Adjust the source voltage R6 to give a reading of 1200 rpm on the low scale. Without changing the setting of the source voltage, disconnect the test leads and switch to the SET position. Adjust variable resistor R8 so the meter reads 1200 rpm on the low scale. After R8 is adjusted, it should never be changed. This completes the circuit calibration.

Prior to each use, the instrument must be adjusted to the proper cylinder setting. Do this before connecting it to the engine. Turn to the SET position and adjust the SET control R6 to give a low-scale reading of 1200 rpm for 6-cylinder engines or 900 rpm for 8-cylinder engines. If you prefer, add cylinder set marks to the dial at these

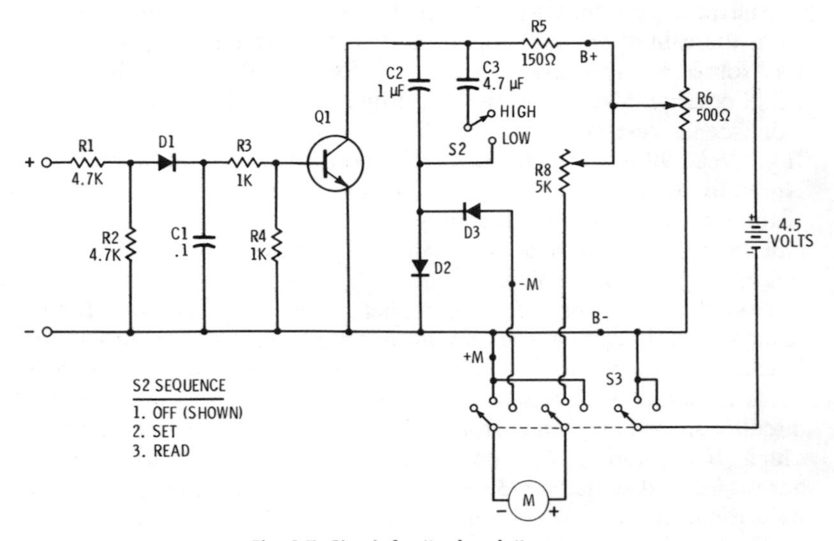

Fig. 2-7. Circuit for "tach only" tester.

points. See Fig. 8-2. For 4-cylinder engines, use the 8-cylinder setting but double the meter readings. Of course, the instrument can be modified to give direct readings on 4-cylinder engines.

USING THE TACHOMETER

The tach is one of the easiest to use of all test instruments. Before connecting it to the ignition system, be sure it is properly calibrated as previously described. The test leads are connected to the distributor primary terminal, either at the coil or distributor, and engine ground. On Ford products, which use a slip-over terminal connector at the coil, a test adapter can easily be fashioned from a paper clip. Observe proper polarity.

The rule is to use the low range for all low speed tests. Operators are sometimes puzzled when they notice a slight difference between the readings of the two ranges. Frequently, tachs give one reading on the low range and another reading on the high range. This is usually due to the nonlinearity of the meter, which, even in good meters, can amount to 2% of full scale. If your tach is properly calibrated, the low-scale reading will generally be the most accurate. It is not so much a question of accuracy as it is of readability; the low scale can be read more closely than can the high scale.

Increasing speed beyond the range of the low scale will not harm the instrument. While the low range is used for most carburetor and idle adjustments, the high range is used mainly to set the engine to proper speeds for such as:

1. Fast-idle adjustments.
2. Charging system tests.
3. Distributor advance tests.
4. Ignition system tests.
5. Transmission tests.

SETTING ENGINE IDLE SPEED

Idle adjustments are becoming more involved as more emission control devices are added. Because each manufacturer has his own procedure, we can give only a general approach. This should be augmented by the manufacturer's detailed method. One requirement is common to all cars: they must be at normal operating temperature prior to adjustment.

On earlier cars, idle adjusting procedures are fairly standard. Two settings are involved: the idle mixture and the idle speed adjustments. The idle mixture adjustment determines the air-fuel ratio for best idling; the idle speed adjustment sets the throttle plate for proper idle rpm (on some cars, the throttle plate is closed at idle and idle speed controlled by an adjustable air bleed).

On cars with two-barrel carburetors, the mixture screws are first synchronized by turning them fully in (gently) and then backing them out equally, about 1½ to 2 turns. Each screw is then turned equally, either in (leaner) or out (richer) to obtain maximum idle speed. This is usually half way between the lean and rich rpm drop-off settings. Some mechanics favor the rich side of the maximum rpm setting. The procedure is the same for single-barrel carburetors, but no synchronization is required.

Idle speed is then set with the throttle stop screw. Be sure the choke is fully open. Sometimes it is necessary, after setting the idle speed, to go back and touch up the mixture screws. Cars with automatic transmissions are frequently adjusted in drive range. Make certain the emergency brake is on and *never* work the throttle linkage by hand.

Many cars have an adjustable fast-idle setting as well as the normal or hot-idle setting. The fast-idle setting usually involves manually moving the fast-idle cam to the position it normally assumes with a partially opened choke and then setting the adjusting screw for the specified fast-idle speed.

The idle adjusting procedure for cars with emission control systems is similar to that above but differs in the technique of setting the mixture screws. Most carburetors on these vehicles have limiter caps on the mixture screws to limit the adjusting range and prevent too rich an idling mixture. On some cars, these screws are factory set and should not be altered. The general practice, on those that are adjustable, is to keep the mixture as lean as possible while still retaining the specified idle speed. Because of the number of procedural variations, the manufacturer's specifications are essential on these cars.

A TACHOMETER INSTALLATION

To adapt the printed-circuit board for permanent installation in a negative-ground car, add a 10-volt zener to the "cal" location and increase R5 to 680 ohms. Omit C3 and calculate C2 for the desired range. Calibrate by shunting the meter. Connect B+ to the ignition switch, B− to ground, and positive input to the breaker points.

3

Testing Points and Condensers

The ignition breaker points and the condenser are frequently accused of all sorts of troubles. Points and condensers do cause trouble, but so do many other things, as we shall see in the following chapters. With periodic checks, it is possible to obtain twice the usual life from a set of points with no loss of performance.

Previously the mechanical or dwell aspects of the points were considered. In this chapter we will be concerned with their electrical functioning and testing.

PURPOSE OF POINTS AND CONDENSERS

The points are actually a switch, electrically no different from any other switch, that must make and break the coil primary current each time a plug fires. A little arithmetic will show that in driving an 8-cylinder car approximately 12,000 miles, the points will make and break over 100 million times (and still have a lot of life left). The ordinary switch can seldom approach this performance.

The mechanical construction of points is familiar to most people. A typical set is shown in Fig. 3-1. The contact discs are cut from rods of special grain-oriented tungsten. These are ground and polished before mounting. The movable contact is given a slightly crowned or convex shape to mate better with the flat stationary contact. Sometimes the stationary contact will have a hole through its middle to improve initial contact and heat dissipation.

If it were not for the condenser connected across the points, they would have an exceedingly short life span. It is the condenser, more than anything else, that gives points their longevity. The condenser acts as a surge chamber or arc suppressor. As in any highly inductive circuit, current tends to keep flowing even after the switch is opened.

If it has no other place to go, it creates an arc between the separating contacts and continues to flow until the contacts separate far enough to break the arc. Such an arc not only burns the contacts but robs the coil of spark energy. This can cause plug misfiring.

The condenser minimizes arcing by providing an alternate path for the primary current. The arc that is not suppressed provides a beneficial "cleaning" effect. At the instant the points separate, a small bridge of molten contact material appears at the point of contact. For a moment, both contacts are linked by this liquefied tungsten. Then the bridge is broken; some of the metal is vaporized and lost, the rest returns to the contacts. A fresh contact surface is created each time the points separate, ready for the next cycle. As this process continues through millions of cycles, a gradual erosion takes place. This erosion eventually wears out the points. But it also contributes to their remarkable lifespan.

Theoretically, new points make only pinpoint contact. All the primary current must pass through this minute area of contact, resulting in high current density and, consequently, greater localized heating. As the contact surfaces gradually erode, they spread over a larger and larger area; the points become "seated-in." Contact heating is minimized and current handling ability is increased. New points can tolerate less abuse than well seated-in points.

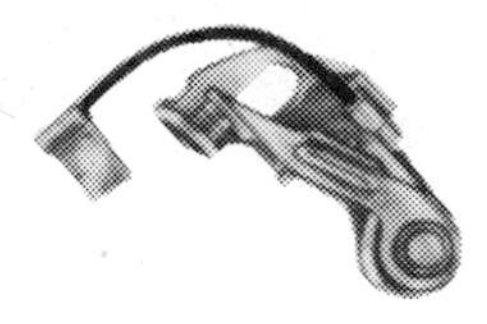

Fig. 3-1. A typical set of points.

THE BALLAST RESISTOR

Excessive current is the prime cause of premature point failure. This causes the familiar "blue points" condition. The dark blue color is actually tungsten oxide, a good insulator. Because points are normally operated close to their maximum current handling capacity (to assure full coil output), there is little margin for excessive current.

Excessive current is caused either by high charging system voltage or an improper ballast resistor. Most cars today use a ballast resistor (Fig. 3-2), either as a separate unit or as a resistance wire connecting the coil to the ignition switch. Some cars, particularly 4- and 6-cylinder compacts, imports, and older 6-volt cars, do not use a ballast resistor. Indiscriminate coil changing, without regard for ballast requirements, can lead to either excessive or insufficient primary current. The results are usually short point life or low coil output.

The function of the ballast resistor, on those cars so equipped, is somewhat of a mystery to many people. Actually, it serves two functions: it reduces coil saturation time (important for high speed) and, when bypassed during cranking, increases coil output for starting. Bypassing during cranking is accomplished by an extra set of contacts in the ignition switch or starter solenoid. The reduced primary resistance offsets the lower battery voltage during cranking to maintain relatively high coil output.

The ability of the ballast resistor to improve saturation time is less obvious. It is well known that when resistance in series with an inductor is increased, the current buildup or saturation time is reduced. This is the familiar L/R time constant relationship. The old 6-volt coils generally had ample output voltage; their problem was in not saturating quickly enough at high speeds. By retaining basically the same coil design, adding a resistor to limit the current to a safe level, and feeding this from a 12-volt system, considerable ignition improvement can be made. Such a 12-volt ignition system can build up in much less time than a comparable 6-volt system.

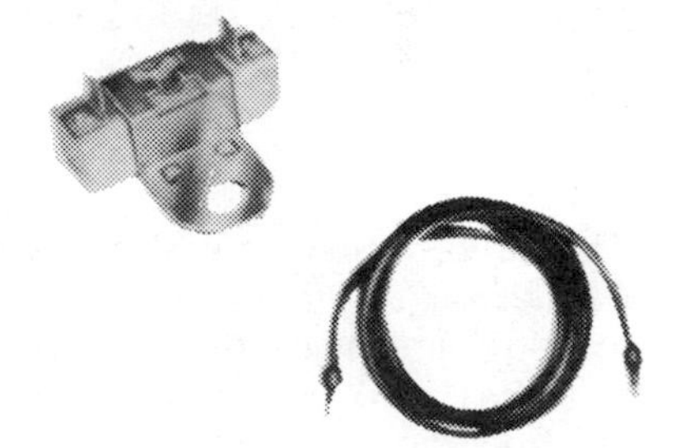

Fig. 3-2. Ballast resistors.

CONDENSER PROBLEMS AND TESTS

The erosion process that gradually wears down the points is controlled, to a large measure, by the condenser. If the condenser capacitance is properly matched to the ignition system, erosion will be equally distributed between the two contacts. If the capacitance is incorrect, metal from one contact will gradually transfer to the other contact. One contact will develop a crater, the other a buildup. This is the familiar pitted points condition. The proper correction is indicated by the minus-minus-minus rule.

MINUS-MINUS-MINUS RULE

If the *minus* contact (usually the grounded one) is *minus* material (has a pit), the condenser is *minus* capacitance (replace with a larger condenser). The reverse is also true; a pit in the positive contact means excessive capacitance.

Today the tolerance on the specified ignition condenser is such that capacitance does not vary enough to cause abnormal pitting. Sometimes, though, the wrong value condenser has been installed.

Short point life can also be attributed to another condenser fault. This is not due to a leaky condenser, as many think, but to excessive series resistance. This effect is shown in Fig. 3-3. The cause of this condition is poor or corroded connections between the condenser plates and the case or pigtail lead. Generally, it takes less than one ohm of series resistance to affect point life. If the resistance increases only slightly above this level, it can also affect ignition performance, even to the point of complete failure.

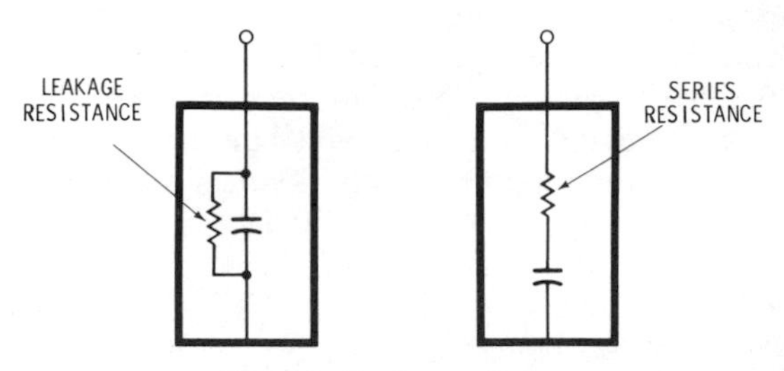

Fig. 3-3. Condenser faults.

This brings up an often-heard question: is it necessary to replace the condenser every time the points are replaced? There are two schools of thought on this subject. The expression "points and condenser" has become a rule with many people. Actually, there is no gradual deterioration in a condenser as there is with the points. Although this was not always true, condensers now are extremely reliable. They can occasionally develop a fault, but this is not normally caused by age. Many experts feel that a condenser is good for the life of the car, while others routinely replace them. Either approach is quite safe.

Because condensers seldom fail, many mechanics have had very little experience with condenser failure. When it occasionally does occur, it is usually overlooked as the source of trouble until all other areas have been covered. Sometimes it is corrected, but never diagnosed, by the wholesale replacement of parts, which includes a set of "points and condenser." The previously mentioned "open" or high series-resistance condenser is sometimes difficult to diagnose. Its effect is easily confused with that of a partially shorted coil, defective plug wires, burned points, defective carburetor or similar faults. Depending on the degree of series resistance, the car may continue to run, but poorly. An easy way to detect this condition is simply to parallel a known good test condenser across the suspected one. If the trouble clears up, its source has been located. Shorted or badly leaking condensers are usually easier to detect; the engine simply stops running.

TESTING POINTS

Now let's go back to the points and see how they can be tested. There are two approaches to point testing: the static or engine-stopped method and the dynamic or engine-running method. The static method can be performed with practically any low reading voltmeter. (See the special voltmeter in Chapter 14.) The procedure is to crank the engine over, if necessary, so that the points are closed. The ignition is turned on and a low-range voltmeter is connected across the points. If the voltage is less than 0.2 volt, point resistance is not excessive (some manufacturers give a limit of 0.12 volt). Typically, it will be 0.05 volt or less.

Remember that not only the point resistance is being measured, but any other part of the circuit that is between the two voltmeter connections. This generally includes the ground circuit for the distributor breaker plate. If possible, it is a good idea to make this plate move (if it is the movable type) to show up any poor grounding.

Static testing, although indicative of point condition, does not duplicate actual point operation. If the points are in poor condition but happen to be making good contact at the time of the static test, they will check OK. The only way around this problem is to test under actual running conditions. This is the function of the dynamic points testing circuit described below.

DYNAMIC POINTS TESTER

The task of the dynamic points tester circuit (Fig. 3-4) is to measure the normally low-voltage drop across the points when they close but to ignore the high ignition voltage when they open.

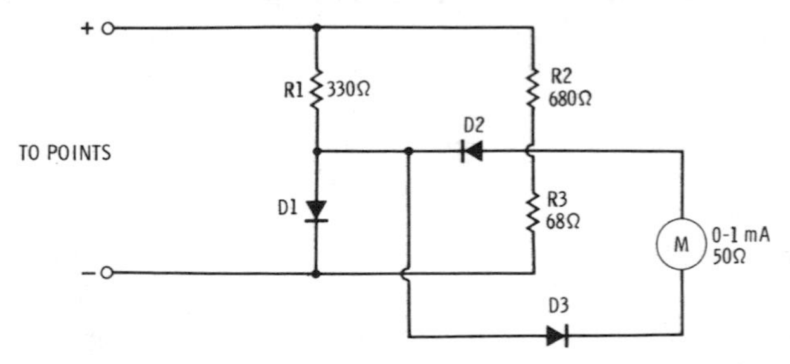

Fig. 3-4. The dynamic points tester.

The circuit works in this manner. When the input voltage is low (below 0.5 volt), neither diode, D1 or D2, conducts. The low input voltage causes a small current to flow through R1, D1, the meter, and the voltage divider R2 and R3. The meter reading is proportional to the input voltage. With proper resistance values, 0.2-volt input causes approximately 10% meter deflection.

However, when the input voltage is high (over 5 volts), a different situation exists. This voltage now causes diode D1 to conduct. The voltage across this diode, as with all silicon diodes, is clamped or held constant at about 0.5 volt. The input voltage also appears across the divider R2 and R3. The voltage across R3 is now higher than the voltage across D1, causing D2 to conduct. The voltage applied to the meter has now been reversed, but D3 prevents any reverse current from entering the meter. The meter current is zero at this time.

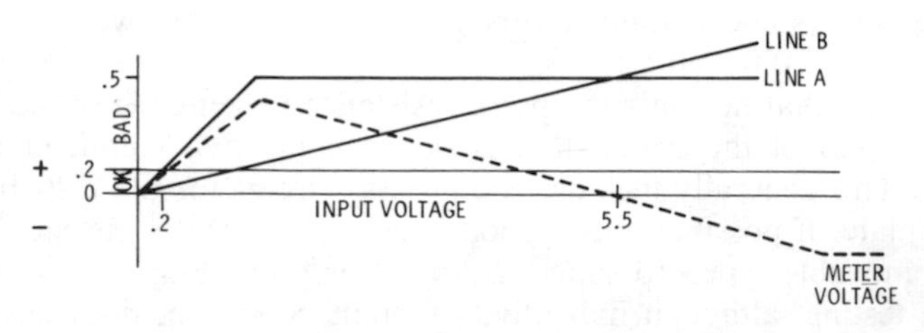

Fig. 3-5. How the circuit measures point resistance.

This process is shown graphically in Fig. 3-5. The dashed line represents the voltage actually applied to the meter and diode D3 combination. Line A represents the voltage across D1; line B represents the voltage across R3. The meter and D3 combination responds to the voltage difference between these two components. As the input voltage increases, D1 voltage increases equally until clamped by the conduction of D1. The voltage across R3 increases linearly, but at an attenuated rate, until it equals the voltage of D1. At this point the voltage difference is zero and the meter current becomes zero. This crossover point should occur at an input of 5 to 5.5 volts so that the circuit will work on 6-volt systems.

As the input increases beyond 5 volts, R3's voltage exceeds D1's voltage and a reverse voltage is applied to the meter. Diode D3 prevents reverse current flow through the meter. Diode D2 clamps this reverse voltage at about 0.5 volt as shown in Fig. 3-5.

As the points open and close, there is either the normally low voltage drop across the closed contacts or a relatively high voltage across the open contacts. The circuit senses only the relatively low voltage across the closed contacts; meter current is cut off during the points' open period. Approximately the first 10% of the meter range is scaled

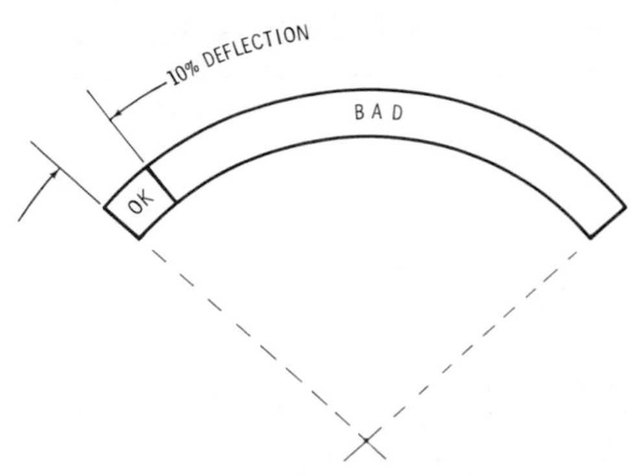

Fig. 3-6. The meter scale.

to represent normal point resistance (actually, voltage drop). The rest of the range indicates abnormal resistance (Fig. 3-6).

If you study the chart in Fig. 3-5 you will notice that there are two input voltage levels that will give a reading in the OK part of the scale. The first, of course, is the normally low voltage drop of the closed points. The second is between approximately 4.5 and 5.0 volts, just below the crossover point in the chart. Points with this much voltage drop could, theoretically, give a reading in the OK range. In practice, this cannot happen; a car cannot run with that much drop across the points.

The advantage of the dynamic points test is being able to "see" the steadiness of the breaker point resistance. This is what indicates whether points are going bad. If the meter reads low and steady in the OK range, you can be quite certain the points are normal. However, if the meter reading drifts around or sporadically deflects into the BAD range, point trouble is developing. The circuit will show the increase in contact resistance long before it affects engine operation. This test can be made at any speed, but is most sensitive to point conditions at lower speeds—approximately 500 to 1000 rpm.

On a few cars, due to the particular design of their ignition systems, you may notice a slight unsteadiness at very low idle speeds. If this condition disappears a little above idle speed, it is not an indication of point trouble. Bad points will continue to show an erratic meter reading.

When new points are installed, you may notice a higher-than-normal reading. This is due to the higher-than-normal contact resistance of points that have not seated-in. After a short while the contact surfaces will be mated better, and contact resistance will drop. In fact, the contact resistance of well seated-in points is so low that it is often below the threshold voltage of the meter diode, D3. Under these conditions the meter shows virtually no deflection.

Table 3-1. Parts List for Dynamic Points Tester

Item	Description
R1	Resistor, 330 ohms, ½ watt, 10%
R2	Resistor, 680 ohms, ½ watt, 10%
R3	Resistor, 68 ohms, ½ watt, 10%
D1, D2	Diode, silicon, 200 volts
D3	Diode, germanium, 1N34 or 1N60 (see note)
M	Meter, 0–1mA, 50-ohms internal resistance

Note: Diode D3 controls the sensitivity of the circuit. Sometimes it helps to parallel two diodes to improve meter responses.

CONSTRUCTION

There are no critical parts in the circuit. Standard ½-watt, 10% resistors can be used, which will provide the proper calibration. Be sure not to interchange the silicon diodes (D1 and D2) with the germanium diode D3; the particular properties of each are essential to circuit operation. A full size printed-circuit pattern is shown in Fig. 3-7. See Table 3-1 for the dynamic points tester parts list.

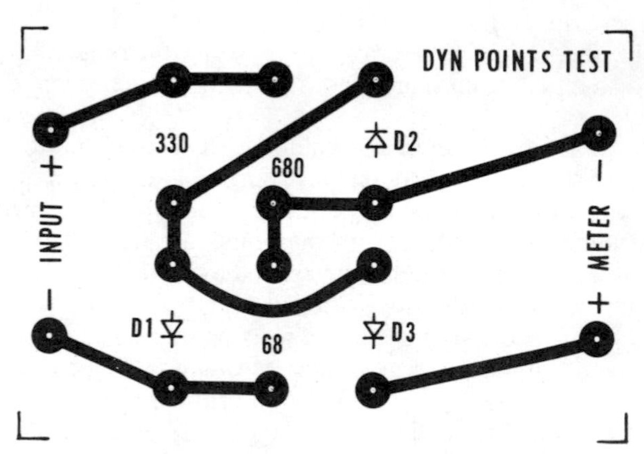

Fig. 3-7. A full-size printed-circuit pattern for the points tester.

The completed circuit (Fig. 3-8) can be checked with a variable 0-12-volt source. With the input connected to this voltage source, the meter reaction should be:

1. Approximately 10% deflection with 0.2-volt input.
2. Increasing deflection to full scale and beyond as input voltage increases to 2 volts.
3. Decreasing deflection as input increases to 4.5 volts.
4. Zero deflection between 4.5 and 5.5 volts and above.

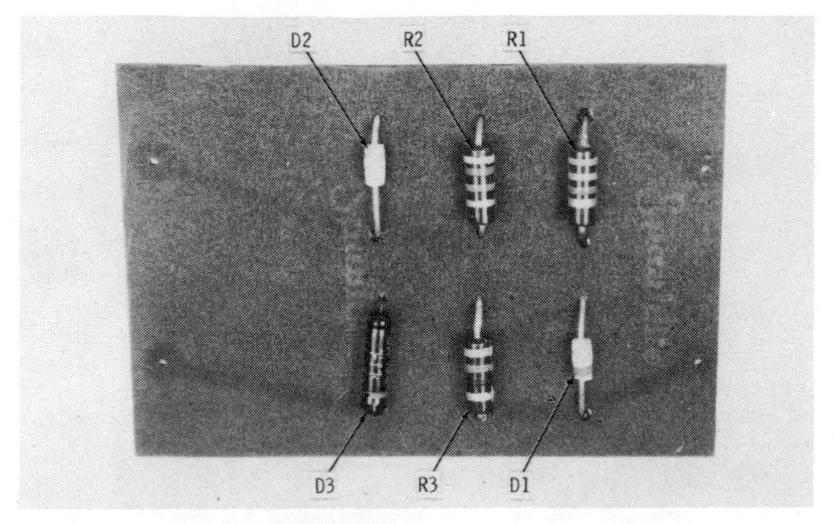

Fig. 3-8. A completed points tester printed-circuit board.

USING THE TEST CIRCUIT

The dynamic points testing circuit is connected, observing polarity, directly across the ignition breaker points—the same as a tach or dwellmeter. If this circuit is incorporated into the Master Analyzer it will be automatically connected to the test leads by the main test selector switch. If this circuit is made into a single purpose instrument, no switch is needed; simply connect the test leads and meter directly to the circuit board.

It should also be remembered that you are testing not only the breaker point resistance, but any other resistance that may be in the distributor part of the ignition primary circuit. This includes the distributor breaker plate ground circuit. Poor grounding of these plates is not unusual. It shows up in the dynamic points test as a sudden meter deflection into the BAD band as engine speed is slowly increased. At a certain speed, the vacuum advance will start to function, causing the breaker plate to move. Any poor grounding usually shows up at this time.

One final word before we leave the subject of points. Years ago it was common practice to file points as a maintenance procedure. Now point filing is considered only an emergency or stop-gap technique to keep the engine running until a replacement can be made. Filing destroys the natural seating surface of the contacts, resulting in dubious and short-lived performance. If the points have deteriorated to the level requiring filing, as periodic checks reveal, they should be replaced.

4

Ignition Testing

In previous chapters we discussed the breaker points and their testing and adjustment. In this chapter we will be concerned with the balance of the ignition system—the coil, cap, high-tension wires, rotor, and spark plugs. Since the basic functioning of this system has been covered, we can consider the types of faults that it can develop.

IGNITION FAULTS

The only function of the ignition system is to fire the proper plug at the proper time. Anything other than this is considered a misfire. Although misfiring sounds like a straightforward type of fault, it can sometimes be confused with a faulty carburetor—particularly when the fault is noticed during acceleration. When localizing ignition trouble, the usual procedure is as follows: see if the ignition system is functioning properly. If so, the trouble is assumed to be in the fuel system—generally, in the carburetor.

An ignition misfire falls into one of two categories: (1) insufficient spark energy to fire the plug gap or (2) sufficient, but misdirected spark energy. Most of the conditions causing these faults can be readily tested. The few that cannot be tested so readily can usually be pinpointed by the process of elimination. Let's consider the first category of misfires.

INSUFFICIENT SPARK ENERGY

Misfires caused by insufficient spark energy are due either to a defective coil or to trouble in the ignition primary circuit. The primary circuit includes the points, condenser, ballast resistor (if so equipped), igniton switch and wiring. We will assume that the points have been previously tested. The balance of the primary circuit can be quickly checked with the following tests.

Checking Ignition Primary Circuit

The condenser could be a source of trouble, but statistically it is at the bottom of the list of ignition troublemakers. If you have not located any ignition trouble with the tests to be described, you can then test the condenser separately, as described in Chapter 9.

The purpose of the ignition primary circuit is to deliver the full, specified current to the coil primary winding. Any excessive resistance in this circuit (other than that designed into it), will reduce primary current and cause misfires due to insufficient spark energy. We can detect excessive primary resistance by measuring the voltage delivered to the input of the coil primary winding. To do this, merely connect a voltmeter between the input primary terminal and ground as shown in Fig. 4-1. Be sure the points are closed. If the system uses no ballast resistor, this voltage should be no more than 0.3-volt less than the battery voltage. A greater difference indicates abnormal resistance; the usual cause is a defective ignition switch.

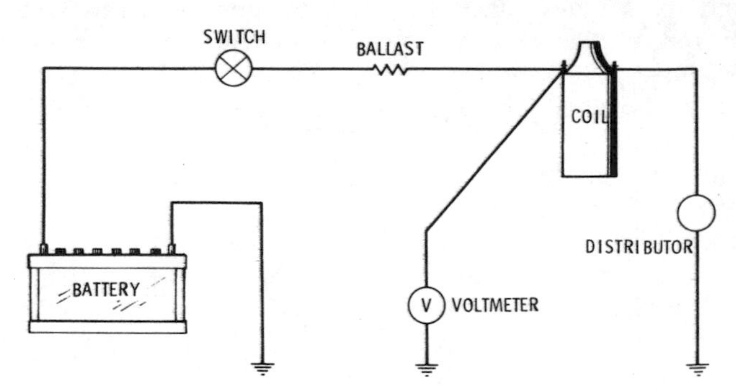

Fig. 4-1. Checking the ignition primary circuit.

If the system uses a ballast resistor, the voltage measured at the coil input will be somewhat less than battery voltage. The voltage difference will depend on the resistance of the ballast and current drain of the coil. The voltage difference is merely the product of these two specifications. For example, if the system uses a 1.8-ohm ballast and the coil draws 3 amperes, the voltage difference is 5.4 volts ($1.8 \times 3.0 = 5.4$). This means that the measured voltage should be 5.4 volts less than battery voltage. A significantly higher or lower difference indicates possible trouble. This could be caused by an improperly matched coil-ballast combination.

Coil Troubles

If the primary circuit proves normal, misfires due to insufficient spark energy are caused by faulty coils. Coils fail for several reasons: either the windings become open or are shorted, or the insulation breaks down. Depending on the nature of the fault, a defective coil can cause either total or partial ignition failure. Fortunately, these faults are readily detected with the proper test circuit. Such circuits can test the coil as a separate component (see coil tester in Chapter 9) or as part of the complete ignition system.

MISDIRECTED SPARK ENERGY

The other cause of ignition misfiring is misdirected spark energy. The spark energy dissipates not at the plug gap but elsewhere. It may leak off through a conductive coating on the plug electrodes (plug fouling) or through any other extraneous path in the high voltage system. This last condition is called insulation breakdown. Both this and the shorted coil condition will be detected with the circuits to be described.

DETECTING IGNITION FAULTS

In a properly operating ignition system, a characteristic waveform will always be observed across the breaker points. This is shown in

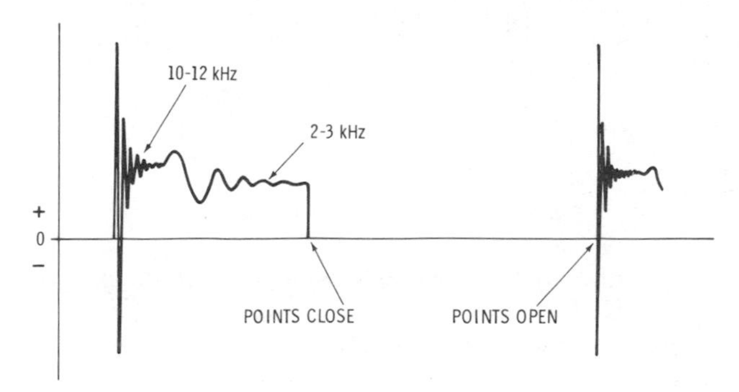

Fig. 4-2. A normal ignition primary waveform.

Fig. 4-2. When ignition faults develop, they usually reflect themselves in this waveform. It can be analyzed either visually, as we will do in Chapter 12, or by specially designed metered circuits. First consider how this waveform reacts in a normal system.

The waveform shown in Fig. 4-2 consists of two distinctive parts. The first is a high-frequency portion, oscillating at about 10–12 kHz, that represents the spark discharge portion of the ignition cycle. When the spark extinguishes, but before the points close, the frequency drops to about 2–3 kHz. The rest of the waveform is essentially a straight line representing the points closed or dwell portion of the cycle. We will examine this waveform in more detail in Chapter 12. For now, notice that almost the entire waveform is positive (assuming a negative ground car); only a small portion of the high-frequency portion goes in the negative direction.

However, it is this negative-going portion that allows us to make a simple yet sensitive and all-inclusive test of the ignition system. Assume for the moment that this waveform represents the ignition cycle for one cylinder in a multicylinder engine. If we lift off the high-tension wire leading to the plug for that cylinder, the plug cannot fire. The coil secondary voltage will build up in the normal manner but no spark current will flow. Under these conditions, the waveform takes a different shape. The normal high frequency portion disappears, since this is present only when the coil is delivering spark current. The low frequency is now greatly enlarged and exhibits a substantial negative-going pulse (Fig. 4-3).

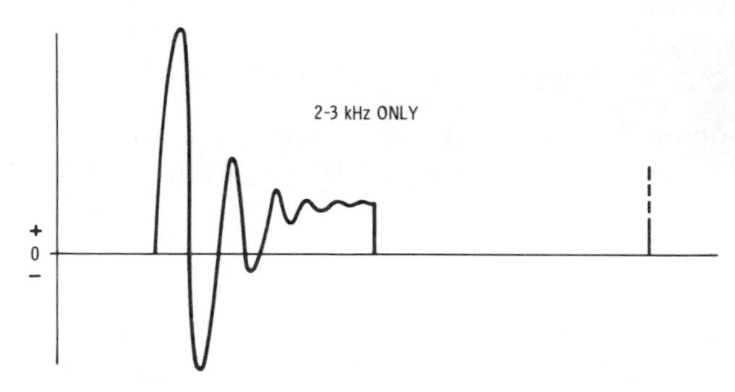

Fig. 4-3. A "no spark" primary waveform.

It is the presence of this negative-going, low-frequency pulse that tells the story. Had there been an insulation breakdown in the disconnected high-tension wire, or in the cap, rotor, or even in the coil itself, the low-frequency negative-going pulse would not have appeared. The waveform would have looked like that of Fig. 4-2. The only negative-going pulse would have been due to the high frequency portion.

As you can see, the negative-going portion of the waveform must be due either to the high- or low-frequency portions, but never to both together. The first indicates that the coil is producing spark current (but it does not tell us where it is going). The second indicates that the coil is producing high voltage but no spark current.

AN IGNITION TEST CIRCUIT

Knowing how the primary waveform reacts under different ignition conditions, we can devise a test circuit to detect the presence or absence of these negative-going pulses. This is shown in Fig. 4-4.

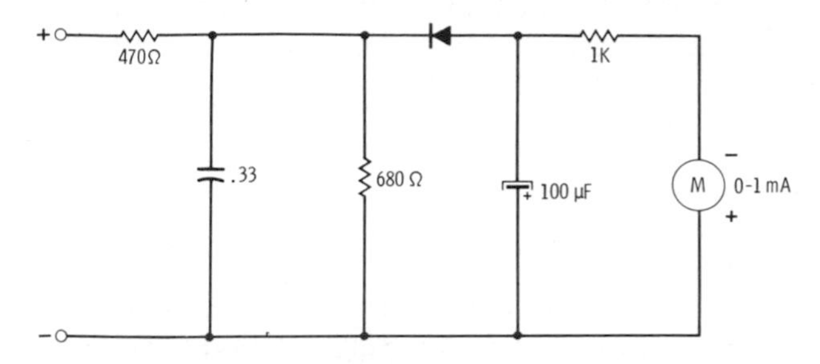

Fig. 4-4. The ignition test circuit.

Basically, the test circuit consists of two sections: (1) a low-pass RC filter followed by (2) a negative peak indicating voltmeter. The filter has a cutoff frequency of approximately 5–6 kHz. This allows only the low-frequency portion of the waveform to reach the voltmeter section of the circuit. Since the voltmeter is negative-indicating, it responds only to negative-going pulses.

THE IGNITION OUTPUT TEST

With the test circuit connected across the breaker points, the ignition system is tested simply by lifting off each plug wire, in turn, and watching the meter reaction. This is called an ignition output test. As each plug wire is lifted, the meter should respond with an up-scale reading. When the plug wire is replaced, the meter should return to zero. No meter reading, when a plug wire is lifted, means the presence of the high frequency portion of the waveform. This, in turn, means that spark current is flowing, even though the plug wire is off. This is a case of insulation breakdown. The exact location of the breakdown can be more or less localized by noting the test results on the other cylinders.

Failure of the meter to respond during these output tests can also be caused by a shorted coil. This absorbs so much energy that the normal, low-frequency coil oscillations are almost completely damped out. Without these oscillations there can be no meter deflection. The results are similar to that shown in Fig. 4-5. It takes surprisingly few shorted turns to cause this—only one or two in the primary or thirty in the secondary. A car can still run with a partially shorted coil; however, it will start to misfire under acceleration or high speed.

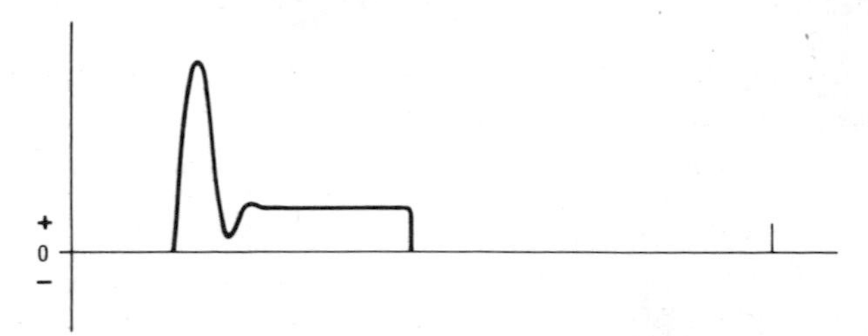

Fig. 4-5. The "no spark" waveform with a shorted coil.

DETECTING IGNITION MISFIRING

Until now we have tested the ignition system by intentionally creating an open secondary or "no spark" condition. This was done by manually lifting a plug wire. However, there are times when the engine itself can create these no spark conditions. These occur whenever the plugs demand more voltage than the coil can produce, or in other words, when the required voltage exceeds the available voltage. This condition is commonly caused by worn spark plugs or defective plug wires.

Worn plugs will function normally except under conditions of high-ignition demands. The most severe demands occur during light-load acceleration. In general, this is when many ignition faults are first noticed. This condition is easily simulated in the shop by quickly accelerating the engine from idle to high speed and back to idle.

If the previous ignition test circuit remains connected during this acceleration test, it will function as a misfire detector. As long as spark current is being produced, the meter will show virtually no deflection. But should a no spark condition occur, such as a worn plug demanding more voltage than the coil can produce, the resulting negative-going low-frequency pulse deflects the meter. This same condition occurs when the plug wires develop excessive resistance. This last fault can also be detected with the secondary-current test described later. This gives you a way of localizing a misfire either to the plugs or the plug wires.

IGNITION RESERVE TEST

The misfire test is frequently called an "ignition reserve test," because you are actually testing to see if the coil has sufficient reserve to meet the highest demands made by the plugs. When the reserve becomes zero, misfiring will occur. To test for ignition reserve, intentionally lower the available coil voltage before accelerating the engine. If no misfiring occurs under these conditions, you know that you will have sufficient reserve when the coil voltage is restored to its normal level.

Lowering available coil voltage is accomplished by two methods. By disabling the charging system prior to the test, the coil will be operating only on battery voltage. This is typically about two volts below its normal level. Also, by adding a capacitor across the test input, as shown in Fig. 4-6, the coil output is further reduced.

It will be apparent that the misfire or reserve test can be made only on an ignition system that has passed the previous output test. Until that part of the system covered by the output test has been proven sound, the results of the reserve test are inconclusive. For example, if the car had a shorted coil there would be no deflection during the output test. Nor would there be any indication during the reserve test, even if misfiring did occur. The negative, low-frequency pulse needed to drive the meter would be missing in both cases.

This one test circuit obviously provides a multitude of testing. Although many factors influence the meter indications, a little reflection will show how the faulty component can be localized. For instance, no meter deflection during the output test on only one or two cylinders means that the trouble must be confined to just those plug wires or to that portion of the cap they are connected to. On the other hand, no meter deflection on any cylinder means the trouble is common to all cylinders. This generally narrows the trouble down to the coil or possibly the rotor.

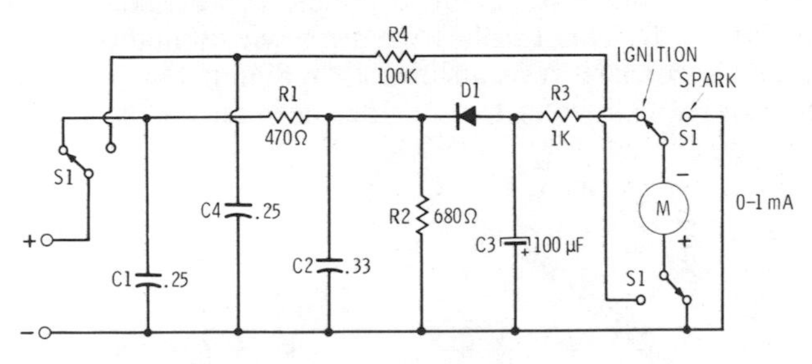

Fig. 4-6. The complete ignition tester.

THE SPARK CURRENT TEST

There is one additional test circuit for pinpointing excessive resistance in plug wires. This is shown in Fig. 4-7. The purpose of this circuit is to measure the relative amount of spark current being delivered to the plugs. It also indicates the polarity of the spark voltage. To keep the plug firing voltages at a minimum, their center electrode should be negative with respect to ground. Reversing this polarity can cause a measurable increase in firing voltage.

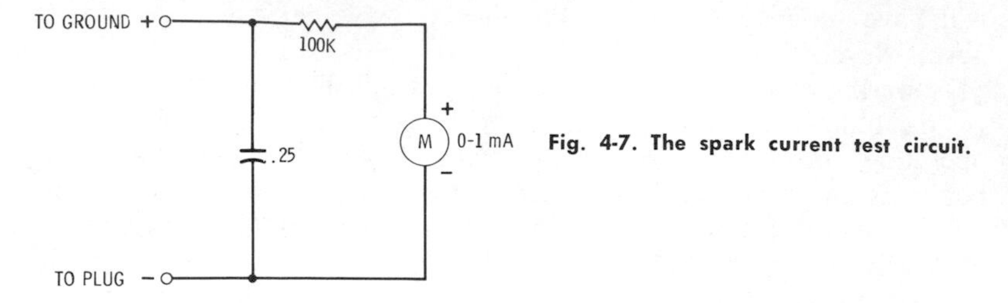

Fig. 4-7. The spark current test circuit.

The test circuit is connected across each plug in turn and the meter reading is noted. A reverse reading is usually caused by reverse primary connection at the coil; the coil is merely connected backwards. Consistency of readings is primarily what you look for. Noticeably lower readings are caused by excessive resistance (or actual gaps) in the affected wires. Since these wires are normally resistance cables to begin with, the readings will vary slightly, depending on the length of the wire. This test should always be made when there is an indication of misfiring during the reserve test. Because most plug wires have insulated plug connectors, it is usually necessary to install test adapters at the plugs to facilitate test connections. These can be readily fashioned as shown in Fig. 4-8.

It should also be pointed out that the spark current test is *not* a test of the spark plugs. The test circuit completely bypasses the plugs. The spark current that normally would have gone to the plug is shunted through the test circuit. In fact, the cylinder being tested does not fire at all. This test has been known by many names: spark current test, secondary resistance test, milliamp test and even, erroneously, as a kV (kilovolt) test. It does not measure coil voltage.

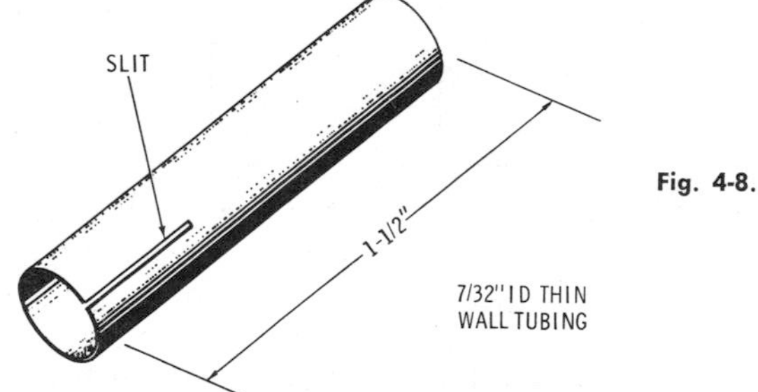

Fig. 4-8. Test adapter for the spark current test.

BUILDING THE IGNITION TESTER

A practical ignition testing circuit (Fig. 4-6), incorporates the functions that have just been discussed. This circuit will make the following tests:

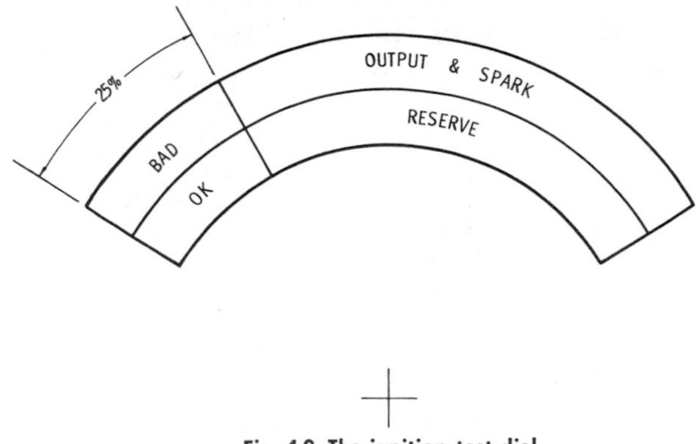

Fig. 4-9. The ignition test dial.

1. Ignition output test.
2. Ignition reserve (or misfire test).
3. Spark current test.

Since we have discussed the principles of output and reserve tests, it comes as no surprise that the same circuit serves for both. The OK band (Fig. 4-9) for the output test corresponds to the BAD band for reserve test and vice versa. The spark current test circuit shares the same meter bands as the output test. To provide comparative reading for the spark current test, a 0-to-10 logging scale is desirable.

If you plan to build this unit (Fig. 4-10) as a separate instrument, instead of incorporating it into the Master Analyzer, you may wish to add a 0–16-volt voltmeter range. This makes for a rather complete ignition analyzer, since it permits voltage checks in the primary circuit. One of the advantages of building your own instruments is that you can tailor them to suit your own needs. Be as plain or fancy as you like.

There is nothing unusual in the construction of the circuit. The printed-circuit layout (Fig. 4-11) is intended to fit the Master Analyzer but is just as easily adapted to single function testers. No calibration is required. In fact, the meter serves merely as a go/no-go indicator. Comparative meter readings (except for the spark current test) have little meaning. The evaluation of the waveform is actually done by the circuit. The tester is quite decisive; either the test is good or it's bad. It is also quite sensitive to ignition faults and will detect trouble even before it affects engine operation. See Table 4-1 for the ignition tester parts list.

Circuit values have been selected to give a meter reading of approximately ½-to ¾-scale deflection on the average car. Occasionally, it may be slightly less than ½ scale or even go beyond full scale.

Table 4-1. Parts List for Ignition Tester

Item	Description
C1	Capacitor, .25 μF, 200 volts
C2	Capacitor, .33 μF, 100 volts
C3	Capacitor, 100 μF, 6 volts, electrolytic
C4	Capacitor, .25 μF, 200 volts
D1	Diode, silicon, 100 volts
M	Meter, 0–1 mA, 50-ohms internal resistance
R1	Resistor, 470 ohms, ½ watt, 10%
R2	Resistor, 680 ohms, ½ watt, 10%
R3	Resistor, 1K, ½ watt, 10%
R4	Resistor, 100K, ½ watt, 10%
S1	Switch, rotary, 3 pole, 2 position

The important thing, however, is that it does deflect when a plug wire is lifted. When all plugs are firing, the meter will normally read zero.

Proper circuit operation is indicated by a normal meter deflection when a plug wire is off and a return to zero when a spark is allowed to jump from that plug wire (this simulates insulation breakdown). If the coil is receiving too much primary voltage (*i.e.*, generator still operating) it may cause spurious breakdown even in a good system. To prevent such misleading test results, keep the voltage at battery level or slightly below.

USING THE IGNITION TESTER

The tester is designed for conventional ignition systems. Electronic ignition systems are normally tested on an individual component basis, such as described in Chapter 9. Some of these systems can be switched back to conventional mode, in which case the following procedures apply.

Ignition Output Test

Connect the circuit input across the breaker points, observing polarity. It is not recommended to have any other instrument connected to the points during these tests. If a tach is used to set the engine speed, disconnect it prior to actually performing the tests.

Before starting the engine, disable the charging system by disconnecting the generator or alternator field wire. This can be done either at the generator/alternator or at the regulator. On cars with plug-in regulators, this is accomplished by disconnecting the plug.

With the engine operating at 1500 rpm, there should be no deflection of the meter. If the meter shows a substantial deflection before making any tests, it usually indicates defective spark plug wires or badly worn plugs.

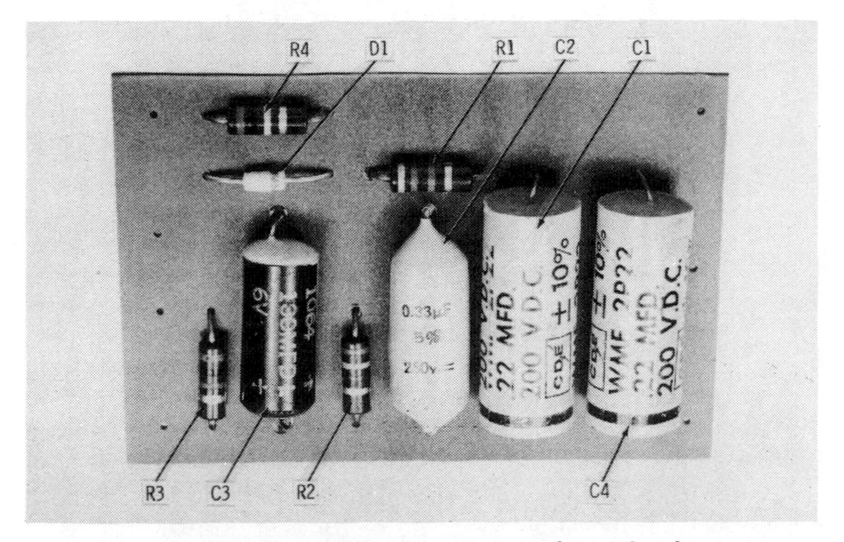

Fig. 4-10. Completed ignition tester printed-circuit board.

In most instances, though, the meter will be indicating zero. If so, you can proceed with the output test. To do this, use insulated pliers (small cartridge type fuse pullers work well) to lift one plug wire at a time from each plug. No more than one plug wire should be disconnected at a time. As each wire is lifted, the meter should show a steady deflection into the GOOD band. When the wire is reconnected, the meter should drop to zero.

If you get normal meter deflection on all cylinders, you know this about the ignition system:

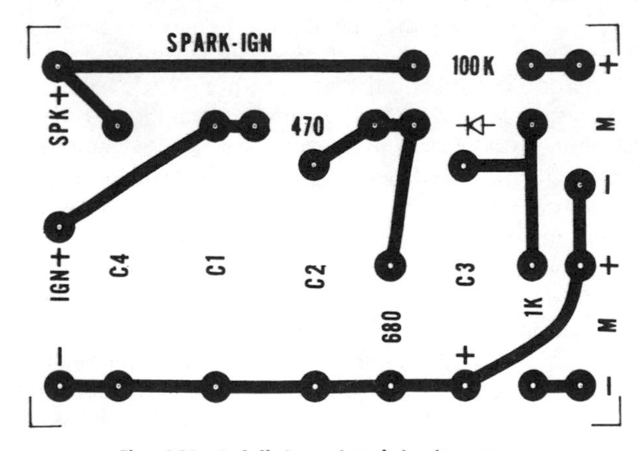

Fig. 4-11. A full-size printed-circuit pattern.

1. The coil is good, and there are no shorted turns or internal breakdown.
2. There is no breakdown in the rotor.
3. There are no cracks or carbon tracks in the cap.
4. There are no insulation breakdowns or leakage in the plug wires.

If you get BAD readings (no deflection) on all cylinders, the trouble could be:

1. A defective coil.
2. A high voltage breakdown in the rotor.
3. Breakdown in the coil to distributor high-tension wire.
4. A carbon track from the center tower of the cap to ground.
5. Battery voltage too high. Turn headlights on.

Visual inspection will usually eliminate most of these possibilities. It is also possible for all plug wires to be bad, but this is rather rare.

If you get BAD readings on only a few plug wires, the trouble is confined to breakdown in just those wires or in that portion of the cap to which they are connected. A carbon track between two adjacent cap towers is not uncommon.

If you get good output tests on all plug wires, you can then make the reserve test. If trouble was detected during the output test, it must be corrected before making the reserve test.

Ignition Reserve Test

Leave the test circuit connected as before, but set the engine to its normal idle speed. Place the tester so it can easily be seen from behind the steering wheel. While sitting behind the wheel and observing the meter, quickly press down the accelerator pedal and immediately release it. Misfiring will be indicated by a sudden deflection of at least one-third scale or more during the acceleration. With a normal system, there will be less than ten-percent pointer movement.

If there were no adverse indications during this test, you can be quite certain of having sufficient ignition reserve. This means that the plugs and plug wires have not deteriorated to the point of causing ignition misfiring. It should be pointed out that this test will not detect plug fouling.

Detecting fouled plugs is done by elimination. If both the ignition output and ignition reserve tests are good, and yet a definite miss develops at certain speeds, you can usually assume that plug fouling is the problem. However, it could also be caused by a compression loss in one or more cylinders. The dynamic compression tester of Chapter 5 will locate the faulty cylinder. Visual inspection of the plug and a conventional compression check should reveal the cause of the trouble.

Most plug fouling, however, occurs at high temperatures, such as that encountered during high-speed or heavy-load driving. Plugs subject to this type of fouling will usually function normally at idling or no-load speeds. This condition can be checked by making a road test with the ignition tester connected in the usual manner. If missing occurs and there is no meter deflection, plug fouling is indicated. On the other hand, if missing occurs and the meter does deflect, it is not caused by plug fouling. In most cases it will be due to worn plugs or plug wires with excessive resistance. The spark current test will quickly indicate the condition of the plug wires. If these are good, the trouble is usually worn plugs.

Plug wear is simply the rounding of the electrodes through normal erosion. This, plus the increased gap, greatly increases their firing voltages. If they are not subject to fouling, they can generally be restored by filing the center electrode to its original flat shape and regapping. In many instances, this can effectively double the life of the plugs.

Some plugs have a built-in suppressor resistor. When this becomes defective, it causes misfiring, just as though the plug were worn. This, of course, can be detected during the ignition reserve test.

Spark Current Test

The purpose of this test is to measure the relative current delivered to each plug. It is primarily a resistance test of the plug wires. Excessive resistance reduces spark current.

The test is usually made at 1500 rpm. With the positive lead grounded, touch the negative lead to each plug terminal and note the relative meter reading. Variations of 15% or more indicate excessive plug wire or suppressor resistance. Remember, the plug is bypassed during this test and has no effect unless it is completely shorted. Also, a reversed reading indicates reversed coil primary connections.

DAMP WEATHER BREAKDOWN

Occasionally, plug wires develop leakage that shows up only during wet or damp weather. If this is suspected, run a grounded "search" prod along the disconnected plug wire during the output test. Any sudden drop in meter reading indicates leakage.

5

Dynamic Compression

If you ask a good tune-up mechanic what are the most important parts of a tune-up, he will probably tell you: Ignition—Carburetion—and Compression. Many automotive specialists refer to this as the Tune-Up Triangle.

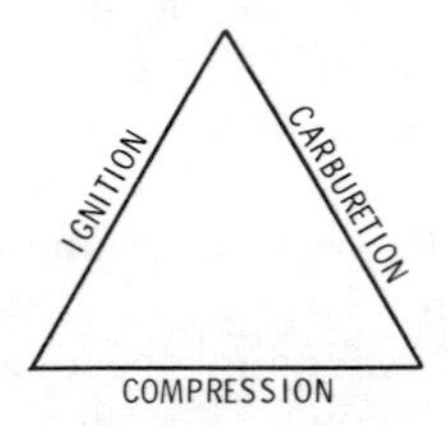

It simply means that all three parts must be present, and in good order, before an engine can be considered tuned. This seems almost too obvious to mention. Yet many people still try to put this triangle together using only two sides.

The side most frequently overlooked is Compression. In fact, without this factor, the other two are virtually powerless. There is no way to compensate for poor compression with either ignition or carburetion. This is why all tune-ups begin—or should begin—with a compression test.

In this chapter we will be considering a "new" way of checking compression. We say new because it is actually a combination of an old technique with a new type of meter circuit. When an old-time mechanic was confronted with a possible power loss in an engine, he would use the "screwdriver-and-ear" method to localize the offending cylinder. He would short out the plug for each cylinder in turn (with the screwdriver) and listen to the effect it had on engine speed. The cylinder having the least effect would be the guilty one.

This technique works reasonably well for older engines but lacks sufficient preciseness for modern ones. The present method is to keep the "screwdriver" but substitute a special tach circuit for the "ear." Although we will not necessarily use an actual screwdriver to short out the plug, we will measure the effect on engine speed with a meter responsive to variations as slight as 5 rpm.

DYNAMIC COMPRESSION TESTING

This new approach is called "dynamic compression testing." A better term might be dynamic cylinder testing, since both compression and ignition (and to a slight extent, carburetion) affect the test results. It should be pointed out that this is not a substitute for the compression gauge. This compression gauge is frequently needed to analyze the results of the dynamic compression test. The role of the compression gauge will be discussed at the end of this chapter.

When dynamic compression testing is incorporated into commercial test equipment, the shorting out (or disabling) of the cylinders is usually done electronically. This is accomplished by connecting a circuit across the points that can be selectively made to appear as a short circuit at any given time in the ignition cycle. This is a convenience rather than a necessity. We can accomplish the same thing by lifting off a plug, just as we did during the ignition tests of Chapter 4. In fact, this technique allows you to make both the ignition tests and compression tests at the same time, merely by flipping the switch on your analyzer.

The change, or drop-off, in engine speed as each cylinder is "killed" depends on the amount of power it contributes. For instance, if the plug of a particular cylinder is fouled out (not firing), that cylinder will show no drop-off in speed when the plug is lifted. A cylinder that is low on compression, and therefore developing less power, will show only a slight drop in speed. A good cylinder, when prevented from firing, will show the greatest drop in speed. The test is primary comparative.

TACHOMETER SCALE EXPANSION

To measure this change in speed, we will use a special expanded scale tach. It is special in several ways. The expanded scale gives it the sensitivity necessary to detect slight differences in speed. It is also adjustable in range; we can shift it to cover any test speed between idle and about 2000 rpm. Lastly, the tach scale reads backwards.

The purpose of the reversed tach range becomes clear when we consider the purpose of the complete instrument which is to show how much relative power each cylinder contributes to the engine.

This power is proportional to the *decrease* in speed when each of these cylinders is prevented from firing. The greater the decrease in speed, the greater the power developed. By using a backward-reading tach, we get an up-scale meter response proportional to cylinder power. Since this measurement is strictly relative, the meter is scaled in arbitrary percentage units.

An expanded scale tach does not start at 0 rpm, as do conventional tachs, but at some predetermined speed. These circuits can be made to give full meter deflection for a small change in speed, for example from 400 to 800 rpm. It is this expansion that gives us the sensitivity necessary to make a dynamic compression test. However, we are not concerned with the actual change in speed, but merely the relative change. This relieves us of the tricky task of calibrating such a circuit.

Although there are a number of ways of accomplishing scale expansion, the most practical for our purposes is the self-powered circuit shown in Fig. 5-1. There are two parts to this circuit—the conventional tach portion and the meter bias portion. The tach portion is a typical self-powered circuit similar to that described in Chapter 10. The bias circuit provides a bias current through the meter that is independent of engine speed. First, consider how these two circuits work together to provide scale expansion in a conventional expanded scale tach.

The meter receives, in effect, two currents. One is developed by the tach circuit and is proportional to engine speed. The other is developed by the bias circuit and is fixed. The bias current flows through the meter in a reverse direction and causes the meter to read backwards until equaled by the forward current of the tach circuit. As the speed increases, the tach current exceeds the reverse bias current, and the meter deflects up-scale. The amount of speed change required to sweep the meter through its full range depends on the meter sensitivity, the value of the tach capacitor, and the voltage of the zener. These factors determine the sensitivity to speed changes.

If the bias current is made adjustable from the front panel, this expanded tach scale can be moved over a wide range of engine

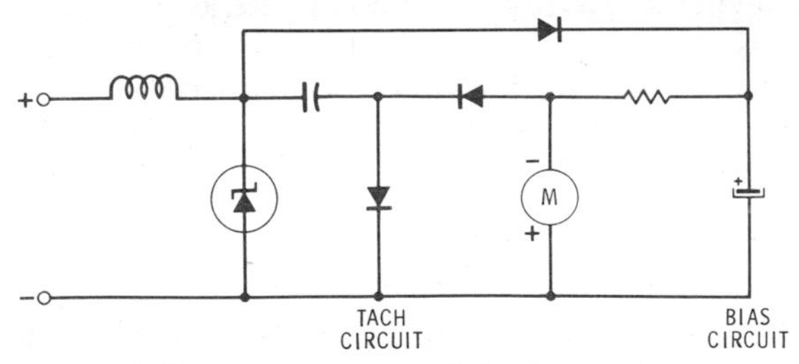

Fig. 5-1. A typical expanded-scale tachometer.

speeds. For example, by varying the bias current, the tach scale can "sweep" any engine speed from idle to about 2000 rpm.

DYNAMIC COMPRESSION TESTER

To change this conventional expanded scale tach into a dynamic compression tester requires only a reversal of the meter connections. The actual test circuit is shown in Fig. 5-2. The bias current set control, P1, is adjustable by the operator from the front panel. For a detailed explanation of the tach portion, refer to Chapter 10. The bias circuit consists of D1, C3, R1 and the set control P1. Diode D1 allows C3 to charge to the zener voltage, but prevents it from discharging through the points. Capacitor C2 is a meter damping device and controls the responsiveness of the meter to momentary speed changes.

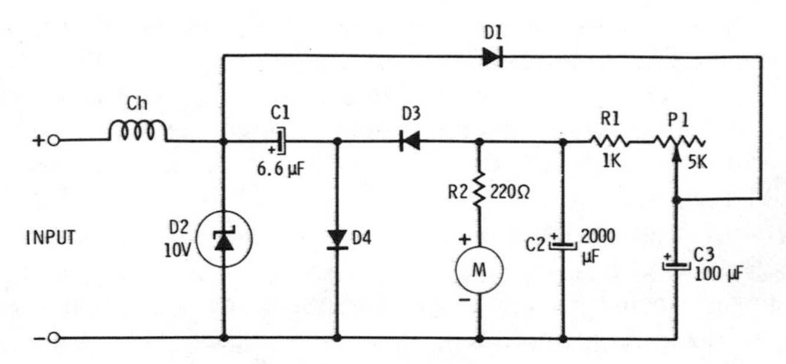

Fig. 5-2. The dynamic compression test circuit.

The sensitivity of the circuit; that is, the amount of meter deflection for a given speed change; is dependent on the zener voltage and the tach capacitor C1. Because of the high value of this capacitor, excessive circuit resistance can reduce the sensitivity. The combined resistance of the meter and R2 should not exceed 400 ohms when using a 2000-ohm choke nor 200 ohms with a 475-ohm choke. However, it is the combined effect of the meter, R2, and C2 that provides the meter damping. If R2 becomes too low, damping will be impaired.

The printed-circuit layout (Fig. 5-3) is intended to fit the Master Analyzer but is just as easily adapted to single function testers. The completed dynamic compression tester printed-circuit board is shown in Fig. 5-4. See Table 5-1 for the dynamic compression tester parts list.

USING THE DYNAMIC COMPRESSION TESTER

Since this instrument is essentially a tach, it is connected to the engine just as other tachs. The engine should be thoroughly warmed

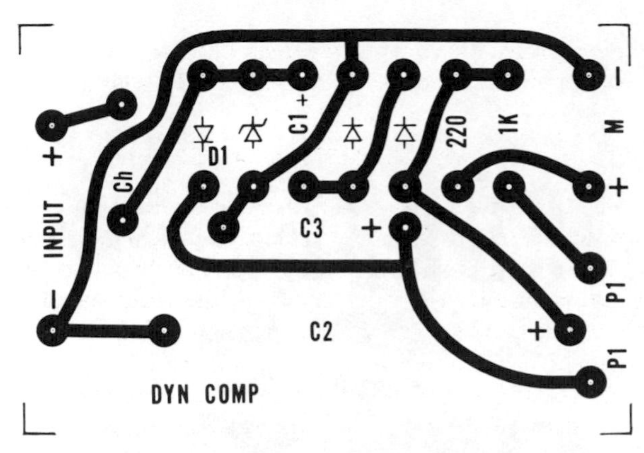

Fig. 5-3. A full-size printed-circuit pattern.

up and the carburetor properly adjusted. There is no one proper test speed, but the following can serve as a guide:

8 cylinder approximately 1000 rpm
6 cylinder 1200–1500 rpm
4 cylinder 1500–2000 rpm

After the engine has stabilized at the test speed, adjust the SET control, P1, to zero the meter pointer. Since modern engines seldom run perfectly smooth, there will be a slight 2 to 3% drift in this zero setting. Using insulated pliers (or midget fuse pullers), proceed to lift off each plug wire, in turn, noting the meter response. The meter will show approximately 10% deflection or more as each wire is lifted. The important thing, though, is the consistency of readings; a lower than average reading indicates power loss in that cylinder. There will always be some variation among even good cylinders.

Table 5-1. Parts List for Dynamic Compression Tester

Item	Description
C1	Capacitor, 6.6 μF, 20 volts, tantalum
C2	Capacitor, 2000 μF, 3 volts, electrolytic
C3	Capacitor, 100 μF, 10 volts, electrolytic
Ch	Choke, 50–100 millihenry, Miller 994 or equivalent
D1	Diode, silicon, 50 volts
D2	Diode, zener, 10 volts, 1 watt
D3, D4	Diode, germanium, 1N34 or equivalent
M	Meter, 0–1 mA, 50-ohms internal resistance
R1	Resistor, 1K, ½ watt, 10%
R2	Resistor, 220 ohms, ½ watt, 10% (see text)
P1	Rheostat, 5K, wirewound (set control)

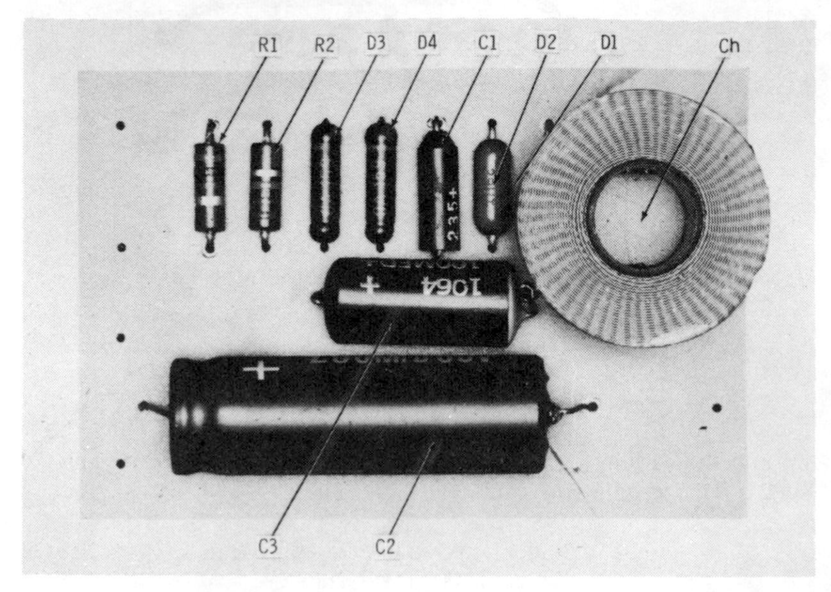

Fig. 5-4. A completed dynamic compression tester printed-circuit board.

The instrument is not confined to single cylinder testing, either. By disabling selected pairs or groups of cylinders, a greater load is placed on the remaining cylinders, which helps to show up any weakness. One technique is to lift off the two plug wires diametrically opposite each other in the cap. Note the combined power output of this pair and then repeat for the remaining pairs. This procedure can easily be done right at the distributor cap.

Another technique is to run one bank of a V8 against the other bank, noting the relative power output during each test. A slightly better way is to disable every other cylinder in the firing order. On a V8, this will be the two inside cylinders of one bank and the two outside cylinders of the other bank. On a straight 6, it will be the first three cylinders against the last three cylinders. Remember, though, the meter is indicating the relative power of the cylinders being disabled, not the ones still firing.

Sometimes, the response of the meter will give a direct indication of the nature of the trouble. For instance, a zero power output, in most cases, indicates a fouled or nonfiring plug. If you get some power output, even though less than average, it is due to compression loss, not ignition trouble. Two equally low readings on adjacent cylinders could mean a blown head gasket. Occasionally, a badly adjusted carburetor idle mixture will cause uneven readings. All low cylinder readings should be further analyzed with a compression gauge. Most manufacturers of these gauges give comprehensive instructions for their use. These should be carefully studied. There is more to using a compression gauge than meets the eye.

CHECKING COMPRESSION WITH A GAUGE

In general, there are three rules to follow when checking compression with a gauge.

First, do not let dirt fall into the cylinders when removing plugs. If possible, use compressed air to blow out the plug before removal. Some mechanics go so far as to unscrew the plugs half a turn and then run the engine a few seconds to blow out any carbon that may have flaked off when they were loosened.

Second, for comparative results (with which you are primarily concerned), remove all plugs. It is not necessary to block open the throttle. For single-cylinder spot checking—although not considered good testing practice—compression can be checked at idle speed.

Third, test each cylinder with the same number of compression strokes, usually four to five. Be sure they are full strokes. Watch the buildup of pressure from the first to the last stroke. Approximately 65–75% of the final pressure should be obtained on the first stroke, 80–90% on the second and 95% on the third. This is a normal buildup pattern.

A "flat" buildup, that is, no significant increase in pressure after the first stroke, indicates valve leakage. A normal but lower-than-average buildup indicates ring leakage. These are not hard and fast rules but merely generalized trends. See the recommendations of the gauge manufacturer.

6

The Volt-Amp Tester

The electrical system is one of the major systems in the modern car. The heart of this system is the charging circuit which must not only keep the battery charged but also supply the power for all electrical accessories. In this chapter we will be concerned primarily with the charging and starter systems and how they are tested.

The fundamental purpose of the charging system is to: (1) replenish any charge taken from the battery and (2) supply the current necessary to operate the full electrical load. Frequently, charging system problems stem not from a fault in the circuit, but from operating conditions. This fact is not always realized but should be considered whenever a complaint is to be analyzed. Many charging system troubles show themselves in the battery; it either runs down or, occasionally, is overcharged. Other indications are short bulb life or noticeable headlight flare. All of these effects should be noted.

Until a few years ago, the dc or generator charging system was the predominant system in use. Now, however, ac or alternator charging systems are almost universally used. The two systems serve the same function, but for testing purposes there are notable differences.

HOW THE DC GENERATOR SYSTEM OPERATES

The dc system consists of the generator, the battery, and the control unit or regulator. The generator contains two circuits (Fig. 6-1)—the field circuit and the armature circuit. The only difference among generators is the method of completing the field circuit. The externally grounded generator is called "Circuit A" and is typical of General Motors and Chrysler products. The internally grounded type is called "Circuit B" and is typical of Ford products. Electrically the two methods are equivalent. However, for certain tests they do require slightly different testing procedures. This will be discussed later.

A small current flows through the field coils and creates a magnetic field. Rotating in this field are the armature windings, which are connected to the commutator. This motion induces a current in these windings. This current, called the main charging current, flows through the armature windings, the commutator bars, the brushes, and into the vehicle's electrical system.

The commutator bars act as mechanical rectifiers. Because of the rotation of the armature, the current induced in it is actually alternating. As soon as it starts to change direction, a new set of commutator bars appears under the brushes, and a continuous though slightly pulsating dc output current results.

The output of any given generator depends on the speed of the armature and the strength of the magnetic field. The speed of the armature, of course, is determined by the speed of the engine and the size of the driving pulleys. A generator does not produce its full rated output until a certain speed is reached. The vehicle designer takes these factors into consideration in specifying a given generator and pulley arrangement.

The only variable available for controlling output is the strength of the magnetic field, or, more specifically, the field current. On some early generators the field winding was simply connected to the armature through a "third brush." No attempt was made to control field current. At a certain speed, depending on the setting of this third brush, output current would be at a maximum. Long trips tended to overcharge the battery, and the remedy was to drive with the headlights on.

From this simple arrangement, we evolved into the modern dc charging system with its three-unit regulator. These regulators are

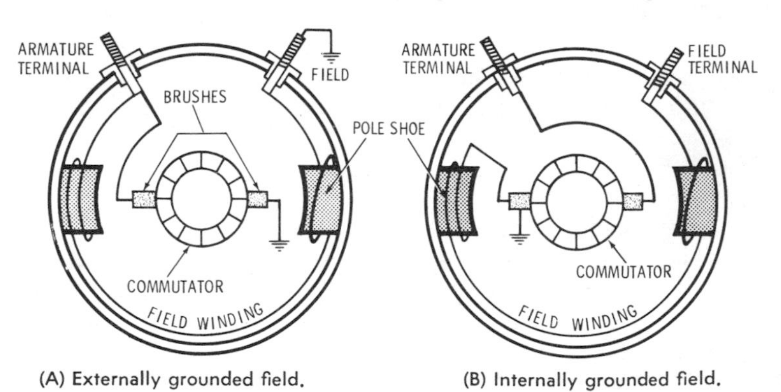

(A) Externally grounded field. (B) Internally grounded field.

Fig. 6-1. The two circuits of the dc generator.

frequently called "voltage regulators," although the voltage regulator is only one of the three units. Let's consider the function of each of these units.

THE THREE-UNIT REGULATOR

The first unit is called the cutout relay. Its sole purpose is to connect the generator to the battery when the generator is operating fast enough and to disconnect it when it is not. (The cutout relay does not "cut out" the generator when the battery becomes charged, as some believe.) It is simply a heavy duty switch in series with the main charging circuit (see Fig. 6-2). It has two actuating windings wound on a common core. The first is many turns of fine wire called a "voltage sensing winding." Being connected to the output of the generator, its strength is dependent on generator voltage. When this becomes

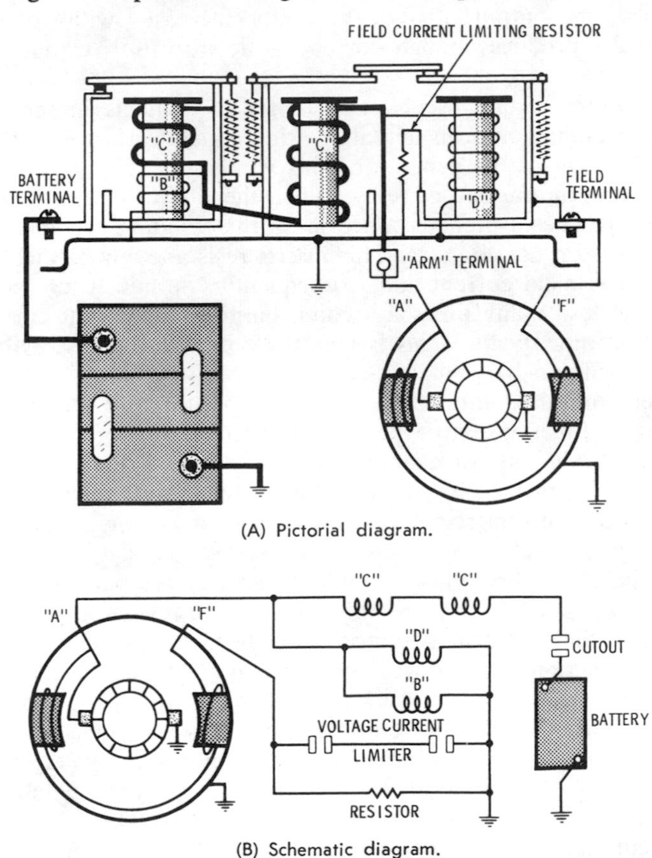

(A) Pictorial diagram.

(B) Schematic diagram.

Fig. 6-2. A three-unit regulator.

sufficiently high (determined by engine speed), the voltage sensing winding closes the cutout relay contacts. The generator is then connected to the battery.

When generator voltage drops to a low value, which can occur at low idle speeds, battery current attempts to discharge through the generator. This reverse current passes through the "current winding" on the cutout relay. The magnetic polarity of this winding reverses or cancels out the magnetic polarity of the voltage winding, and the cutout relay contacts open. If it were not for this reverse current winding, the cutout relay would act as a latching relay. Once closed by the generator, it would be kept closed by the battery—at least until the battery completely discharged itself through the generator.

The second unit is called the current regulator. Its purpose is to safeguard the generator from producing too much current. Unless controlled, the output of a dc generator increases with speed and can actually produce enough current to destroy itself through overheating.

The current regulator consists of a set of contacts in series with the field windings and an actuating winding of heavy wire in series with the output of the generator. This winding is similar to the current winding on the cutout relay. When the output current from the generator reaches a predetermined level, this winding becomes strong enough to open the contacts. This inserts resistance in the field coils, cutting down field current and, consequently, output. These contacts open and close many times a second, limiting the output current to its predetermined value. This is why these units are called "vibrating contact regulators."

Under normal conditions the current regulator unit seldom comes into play. It functions only when the electrical load is great or the battery is in a low state of charge. Most of the time the output of the generator is controlled by the third unit—the voltage regulator.

Just as the current regulator puts a limit or ceiling on the output current (to protect the generator), the voltage regulator puts a ceiling on the generator voltage. This is to protect the battery and electrical accessories. Of the three units, the voltage regulator is the workhorse, and, therefore, the one most likely to give trouble.

In construction, the voltage regulator is quite similar to the current regulator. Instead of a current winding, it has a voltage sensing winding, much like that of the cutout relay. This winding, being connected to the generator output, responds to generator voltage. When it reaches a predetermined level, the voltage regulator contacts open and resistance is inserted into the field windings. This reduces generator output. The resulting vibrating action of the contacts maintains a relatively constant generator voltage.

The question is sometimes asked: How does the *voltage* regulator control the charging *current* going into the battery? Actually, the battery is self-regulating. Assume that the battery's state of charge is reflected in its voltage. The charge current going into a battery, then, is determined by the difference between its own voltage and the voltage of the charging source (generator or alternator). When the battery is discharged, its voltage is low and, as a result, the voltage difference is high. This causes a high charge rate. As the battery comes up in charge, its voltage increases. Since the charging voltage remains constant, the voltage difference decreases, decreasing the charge rate. When the battery is fully charged, the charge rate drops to a very low value. This assumes, of course, that the charging voltage is properly regulated.

HOW THE AC CHARGING SYSTEM WORKS

By comparison, you will see that the ac or alternator charging system (Fig. 6-3) is quite simple. You will find neither the cutout relay* nor the current regulator. The voltage regulator still remains, however. Neither will you find the commutator and brushes, needed for the rectification of the armature current. In a mechanical sense, the alternator is the opposite of the generator. In an alternator, the stator windings (which are the equivalent of the generator armature windings) are stationary; in these stator windings, the rotor or field winding revolves.

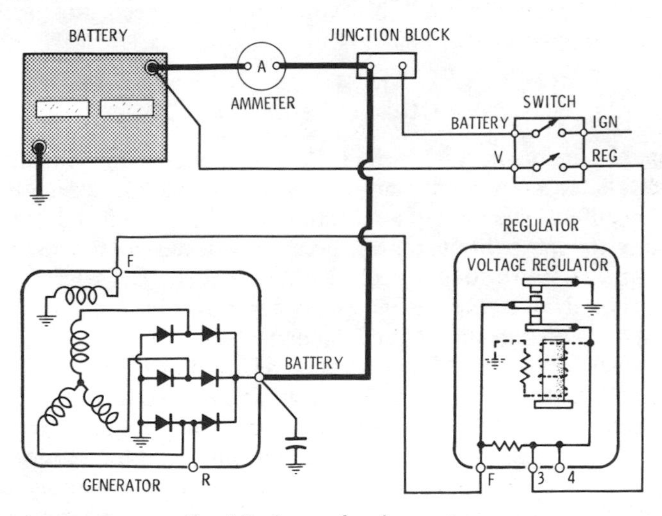

Fig. 6-3. An ac charging system.

*A few ac systems use a circuit breaker, which is similar to a cutout relay.

Rectification of the stator winding current is accomplished by a system of diodes. Since the stator windings comprise a three-phase system, six silicon diodes are used in a full wave rectifier configuration. Because of their low reverse leakage current, no cutout relay is required to disconnect the battery from the alternator.

The vibrating contact voltage regulator used with alternators is quite similar to that used in dc systems. See Fig. 6-4. Many of these are built on the "double contact" principle to provide better voltage regulation at high engine speeds. The extra contact simply shorts out the field winding when the system voltage reaches a certain level, thus reducing field current to zero.

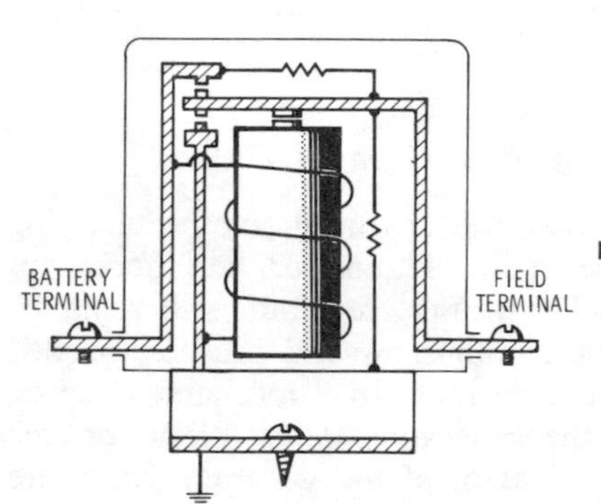

Fig. 6-4. A double contact voltage regulator for alternators.

Due to a characteristic of alternators, they will not produce more than their design current. This eliminates the need for a current regulator.

THE SOLID-STATE REGULATOR

Since alternators require only voltage regulation, this function can easily be handled by solid-state circuits. In principle, the solid-state regulator differs little from the vibrating contact regulator. The method of each is to vary field current between two levels by means of rapid switching. From a testing standpoint they can be considered equivalent. A typical solid-state regulator is shown in Fig. 6-5.

The unit works in this manner. When alternator voltage rises to a certain level (due to full field current), zener diode Z conducts, sending the driver transistor DR into conduction. This back-biases the output or field current transistor into cutoff, stopping the flow of field current. The collapse of the magnetic field in the rotor reduces alternator voltage. When the voltage falls below the conduction level of Z, driver transistor DR is cutoff, which drives the output transistor into saturation. Full field current then flows and the process repeats itself, as rapidly as several thousand times a second.

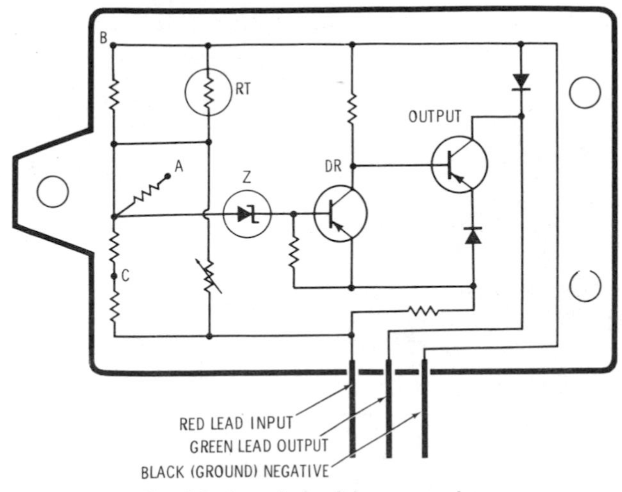

Fig. 6-5. A typical solid-state regulator.

As you can see, the conduction level of the zener is determined by the divider ratio. In some regulators, this ratio (and consequently the voltage regulator setting) is fixed. In others, it is adjustable. Notice also the temperature sensitive thermistor RT, which is selected to give a somewhat higher voltage setting during cold weather. Thus, it is important to know the temperature of the regulator prior to measuring the voltage setting. This fact applies to vibrating regulators also. Unless otherwise specified, most regulator specifications are given for normal operating temperatures.

From a testing standpoint, which is what we are primarily concerned with, these constitute the essential similarities and differences between ac and dc charging systems. In spite of the comparative complexity of the charging system, the instrument used for testing it is quite simple. This is commonly known as the volt-amp tester. This instrument sometimes contains a built-in loading device to facilitate certain tests, in which case it is called a "charging system analyzer." However, by following the procedures at the end of this chapter, all of the basic charging system tests can be made with the volt-amp tester described below.

THE VOLT-AMP TESTER

This is one of the simplest of the automotive testers (Fig. 6-6), being nothing more than a combination voltmeter and ammeter. The voltmeter covers two ranges, 0–4 and 0–16 volts. The low range is primarily for voltage-loss measurements. By using 1% resistors for the voltmeter multipliers, no circuit calibration is required. However,

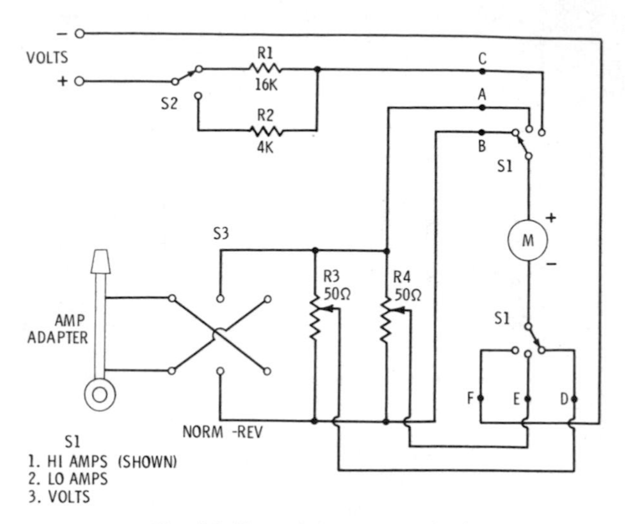

Fig. 6-6. The volt-amp tester circuit.

these can be substituted by hand-selected standard resistors or combinations of resistors. The proper combination is shown by the meter reading agreeing with the voltage source.

The voltmeter can be checked in this manner. If a good, 12-volt storage battery that has just been fully charged is allowed to stand, without discharging, for 8 to 12 hours, its voltage will be 12.6 ± 0.2 volts.

The ammeter is also a dual-range instrument. The 0–80-ampere range is for charging-system tests and the 0–400 range for starter tests. Although a polarity switch is part of the circuit, the meter polarity is automatically reversed between the low and high ranges. This is solely for the convenience of the operator; the current always reverses between starter and charging tests. The only time the polarity switch is needed is when the ammeter shunt is connected to the negative battery post or during special tests.

The accuracy of the ammeter depends on the accuracy of its calibration. If a known accurate ammeter is not available for comparison, the circuit can still be calibrated by following the procedure described in Chapter 10. Once the low range is calibrated, it can be used as a comparison ammeter to calibrate the high range. Merely trip the polarity switch to give an upscale reading.

A full-sized printed-circuit pattern is shown in Fig. 6-7. As with the other test printed-circuit boards, this pattern can be used in a single purpose instrument or incorporated into the Master Analyzer. Even when built into the Master Analyzer, the instrument uses its own test leads; only the meter is common to the other circuits. The completed volt-amp tester printed-circuit board is shown in Fig. 6-8. See Table 6-1 for the volt-amp tester parts list.

The functions of voltmeters and ammeters is covered in basic electricity texts and need not be repeated here. Construction is quite simple. To aid in wiring the switch, the letter codes on the printed-circuit board correspond to those in Fig. 6-6. The most important part of the tester is the battery-post adapter shunt shown in Fig. 6-9. The only critical material is the oil hardening drill rod. This is used because of its resistivity; do not substitute soft steel and do not harden. For batteries with side mounting cables you will need the proper adapters, which are available from automotive parts jobbers.

Details of the meter scale can be seen in Chapter 8. Although there are four ranges in the instrument, only three scales are needed. The 4-volt range can be read from the 400-ampere scale. Since the low-voltage range is used only occasionally, this presents no great inconvenience.

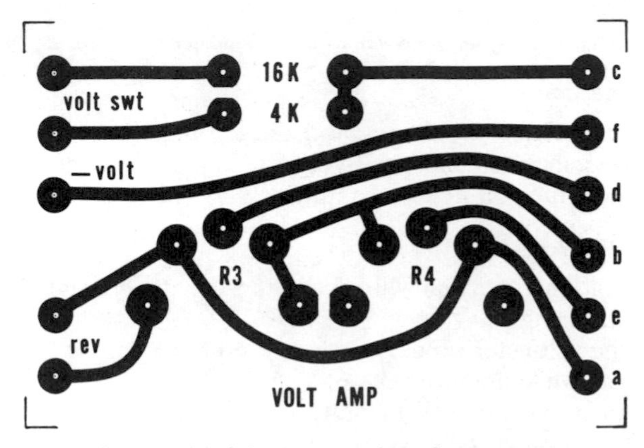

Fig. 6-7. Printed-circuit pattern for volt-amp tester.

USING THE VOLT-AMP TESTER

The volt-amp tester is the basic instrument for practically all electrical system testing. The greatest use of this instrument is in starter and charging system testing. To be meaningful, the test results must be compared with the manufacturer's specifications for the units being tested. For example, the fact that an alternator produces 45 amps means little if you do not know how much it *should* produce. The most important specifications you will need are generator or alternator output current, the voltage regulator setting, and the starter amperage drain. For dc systems, you should also know the cutout relay closing voltage, the opening amperage, and the regulator setting. Most specifications are based on normal operating temperature.

Fig. 6-8. A completed volt-amp tester printed-circuit board.

Basic Connection

1. Disconnect the positive cable from the battery, and connect the adapter shunt to the positive post and the disconnected cable.
2. Connect the voltmeter leads directly to the battery posts.

Cranking Voltage Test

1. Pull the high-tension wire from the coil to prevent the engine from starting.
2. Set the voltmeter range switch to the proper range; and note the voltage while cranking the engine.
3. This is a quick check of battery condition (see Chapter 13 for detailed tests). If the voltage is 9.6 volts or more (4.8 volts for 6-volt systems), the battery is serviceable, and you may proceed with the starter test. If the voltage is low, this is an indication that something is wrong. The trouble will either be a de-

Table 6-1. Parts List for Volt-Amp Tester

Item	Description
R1	Resistor, 16K, ½ watt, 1%
R2	Resistor, 4K, ½ watt, 1%
R3	Potentiometer, 50 ohms, CTS Type 115 or equivalent
R4	Potentiometer, 50 ohms, CTS Type 115 or equivalent
S1	Switch, rotary, 2 pole, 3 position
S2	Switch, toggle, spdt
S3	Switch, toggle, dpdt
M	Meter, 0–1 mA, 50-ohms internal resistance

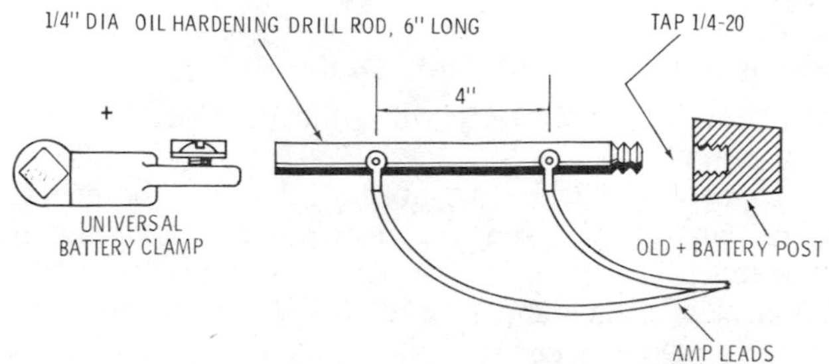

Fig. 6-9. The ammeter battery post adapter shunt.

fective battery, excessive starter current drain, or a battery which is partially discharged because of a charging defect, slow driving, or electrical leakage.

Starter Amperage Drain

1. Set test selector switch to the high-amperage range.
2. Crank engine without starting, and note current drain and speed of cranking.
3. Normally, this should be between 150 and 225 amperes.
4. If cranking speed appears normal but current drain is high, a defective starter is indicated. Slow cranking speed with normal current drain indicates excessive resistance, such as a poor connection somewhere in the starter circuit.

Alternator Output (or Current Regulator Setting for DC Systems)

1. Crank the engine for approximately 10 seconds, without starting, to partially discharge the battery.
2. Reconnect the coil wire. Have *all* accessories *off*.
3. Set the test selector switch to the low amperage range.
4. Start engine and quickly bring speed up to 1500 to 2000 rpm while watching the meter. Use reverse switch if necessary. The highest amperage reading noted will be the alternator output current* (or the current regulator setting on dc generator systems). Compare with specified amount. If it is low, check belt tension first before assuming other trouble. If this is normal, the trouble could be either in the alternator (or generator) or in the regulator. To localize, repeat this test, but bypass the regulator (see below).

Note: Alternators should also be checked with the dynamic diode test described in Chapter 7. Certain diode troubles do not always show up in the output test.

---

*It will be about 5 amperes less than actual output since ignition current is not measured. Add this amount to your reading.

Regulator Bypassed Output Test (Optional)

1. This test is required only when the previous test shows low or zero output.
2. Disconnect the field wire at the alternator or generator.* On many cars, this is just a matter of pulling a plug. Do not let this wire touch ground.
3. Connect a short jumper wire to the alternator/generator field terminal. Do not connect the other end of the jumper at this time.
4. With the tester set as for the previous test and the engine at the same speed, momentarily touch the free end of the jumper lead to the output terminal of the alternator/generator and note the ammeter reading. (On General Motors and Chrysler products using generators, touch the jumper to ground.)
   a. If the output is now normal or above, the trouble lies in the regulator.
   b. If the output is still low or zero, the trouble lies in the alternator/generator.

   Do not leave the jumper connected any longer than is needed to read the meter. Since this bypasses the regulator, the system voltage can go higher than normal.

Voltage Regulator Test

1. After making the output test, continue running the engine until the charging current drops to about 10 or 15 amperes. This may take several minutes or more if the battery was previously in a discharged state.
2. Set the test selector switch to the proper voltage range.
3. Operate the engine at 1500 rpm and note the voltage reading.

(Note: Some manufacturers specifiy that the voltage regulator setting be measured at the regulator. If so, connect the voltmeter leads to the regulator battery terminal and ground.)

4. The voltage regulator setting should be within the manufacturers specified range. Be sure the system is at normal operating temperature, since many regulators are temperature sensitive.

Note: Double contact regulators, for most accurate results, should be tested against a fully charged battery. A battery can be considered fully charged, for test purposes, when the normal charge rate drops below 10 amperes with the engine at cruising speed.

---

*Years ago, mechanics seldom bothered to disconnect this wire. Failure to do this on a modern, double contact regulator can cause instant damage. When in doubt, disconnect.

5. Many regulators are adjustable. However, the need for adjustment should be indicated by battery condition. If the battery has been maintained in a fully charged state without excessive water consumption, you may assume that the voltage regulator setting is proper for that particular vehicle. On the other hand, if the battery is continuously in a partially discharged state, or uses considerable water (over one ounce per cell per 1000 miles), the regulator setting may be too low or too high. Seldom does it have to be changed more than 0.2 or 0.3 volt. The adjusting method for adjustable-type solid-state regulators will be apparent upon examination. The vibrating contact types are adjusted by varying the spring tension on the relay armature. Only a very slight change in tension is required.

Cutout Relay Test (for DC Generator Systems Only)

1. Connect the voltmeter leads to the regulator *armature* or *generator* terminal, not the *battery* terminal.
2. Set the test selector switch to the proper voltage range.
3. Reduce engine speed until the voltmeter reads 2 or 3 volts below battery voltage. The cutout relay should now be open.
4. Slowly increase engine speed while watching the voltmeter, until you notice a slight jump in the voltmeter reading. This will be the closing voltage of the cutout relay.
5. Turn to the low amperage range and increase speed to produce a charge rate.
6. Slowly reduce engine speed until the ammeter shows a discharge (use reversing switch if necessary). Continue to reduce speed, noting the greatest discharge current just before the ammeter returns to zero. This is the reverse current opening of the cutout.
7. The cutout-relay closing voltage should be at least 1 volt below the voltage-regulator setting. The reverse current opening should not exceed 8 amperes. Closing voltage is controlled by the spring tension on the relay armature.

7

Alternator Testing

Although the alternator, in many respects, is equivalent to the dc generator, the two are not similar. One major difference, from a testing standpoint, is the effect of diode failure on the output of the alternator. A diode can either open or short, and each failure has its own characteristic effect.

DIODE PROBLEMS

An open diode can frequently go unnoticed. This type of failure has slight effect on the output of the alternator. If just one of the six diodes should open, the output may drop by only 3 to 5 amperes. In many cases this is not enough decrease to be noticed during an output test such as that described in Chapter 6. Most of the time the alternator does not operate at full output; therefore, there is sufficient current to keep the battery charged and supply a moderate electrical load. However, this means that the full output, when demanded, must be carried by the remaining good diodes. This can cause overloading of these diodes and further diode failure. For this reason, early detection of this trouble is important.

A shorted diode, on the other hand, seldom goes unnoticed. When just one diode shorts, the alternator output drops by 50% or more. Although this may suffice for daylight driving, nighttime driving will usually discharge the battery.

An open or shorted diode will commonly cause a characteristic sound in the alternator. However, this is not a reliable indicator of diode trouble, as it takes a well-trained ear to detect it. Also, the pitch and intensity varies among the many types of alternators.

DIODE TESTING

Because of the particular diode problems that can develop in an alternator and the different ways in which they show up, it became necessary to develop a new test circuit. The purpose of this circuit is to test the diodes while the alternator is still attached to the engine. Such a circuit, of course, eliminates much needless removal of the alternator for bench testing. However, if this on-the-vehicle test indicates diode trouble, the alternator must be bench-tested to locate the defective diode(s). A suitable bench tester and testing procedures are discussed in Chapter 14.

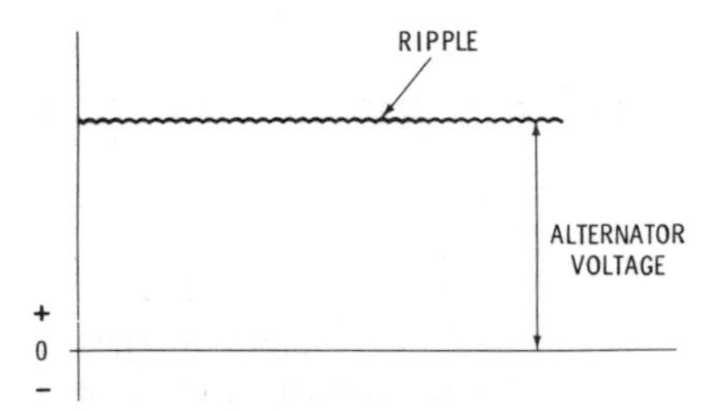

Fig. 7-1. The normal ac ripple of an alternator.

The on-the-vehicle diode test circuit is known by several names. "Dynamic diode tester" and "ripple tester" are two common names used. The latter, perhaps, best describes the principle of the tester. Although the alternator produces dc current, it is actually a rectified ac current (3 phase) and therefore has the characteristic of ac ripple superimposed on the dc level (see Fig. 7-1). Normally, this is a relatively smooth ripple, typically about 0.2 to 0.5 volt peak-to-peak. A diode failure drastically changes this pattern. Typical faulty diode patterns are shown in Fig. 7-2.

Observing such a pattern is easily done with a scope. Some automotive ignition scopes have an adapter especially for this purpose. (See Chapter 12.) However, this pattern can be just as easily measured with a suitable instrument. In its most basic form, such an instrument consists of a low-range ac voltmeter in series with a blocking capacitor. The blocking capacitor keeps out the dc system voltage

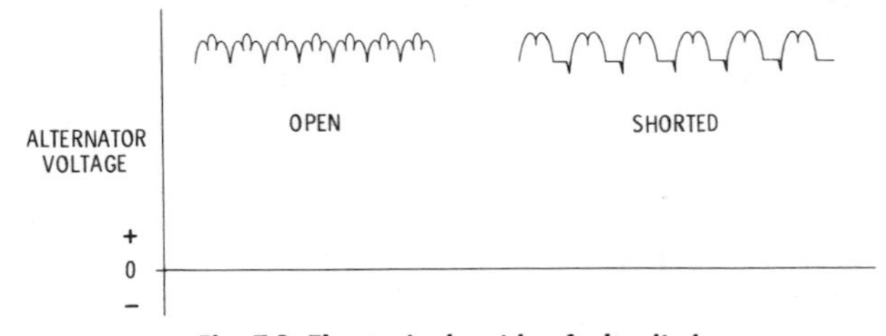

Fig. 7-2. The ac ripple with a faulty diode.

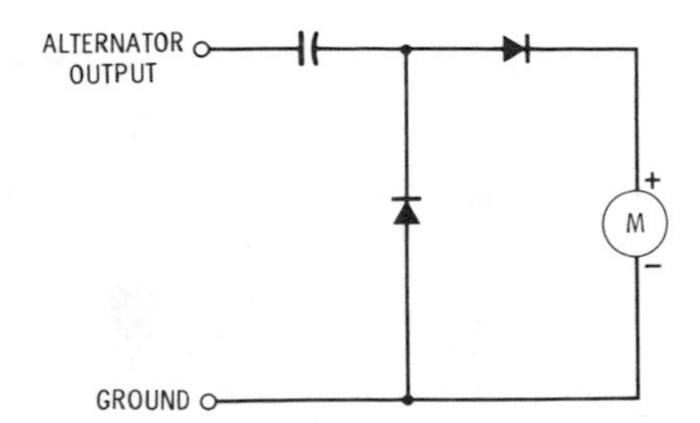

Fig. 7-3. A basic diode ripple test circuit.

but allows the ac ripple voltage to pass through. When a diode fault occurs, this ac ripple increases in amplitude and causes a high reading on the meter. A typical circuit of this type is shown in Fig. 7-3.

For this basic circuit to work requires that additional resistance be added to the main charging circuit. This is necessary because the normal charging circuit resistance is not high enough to develop a readily measurable ripple voltage. Usually, a .25-ohm resistor is added between the alternator and battery for testing purposes.

By using a more sensitive circuit, a satisfactory test can be made using only the normal circuit resistance. This eliminates the need for inserting a test resistor into the charging system and thus simplifies the test procedure. The details of such a circuit are shown in Fig. 7-4. Essentially, it is an ac amplifier that derives its dc operating potential from the system being tested. The superimposed ac ripple is fed into the base of the transistor through C2, driving it into conduction during the positive part of the cycle. The resulting collector current is reflected in the meter reading.

To assure that sufficient ripple voltage is developed, the alternator should be producing a fairly high charge rate. This can be done by partially discharging the battery prior to testing by cranking the engine for 10 to 15 seconds. Pull the coil wire to prevent starting. Normally, a good alternator will show only a slight residual meter deflection. A bad diode can cause anywhere from a ⅓-scale to off-scale deflection. The slight residual meter deflection is produced by the collector-emitter resistor R4. It tells you that the test leads are con-

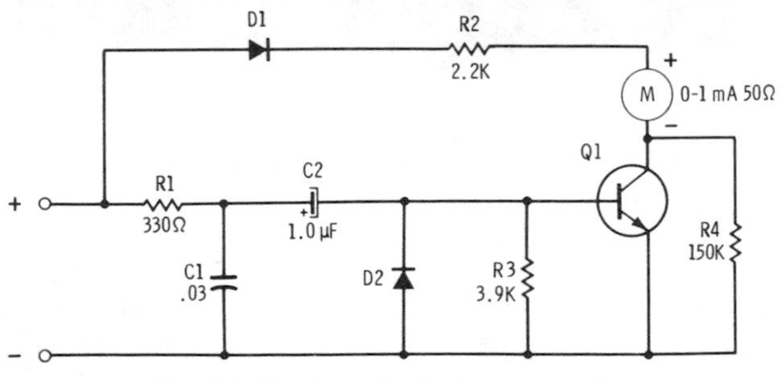

Fig. 7-4. The dynamic diode test circuit.

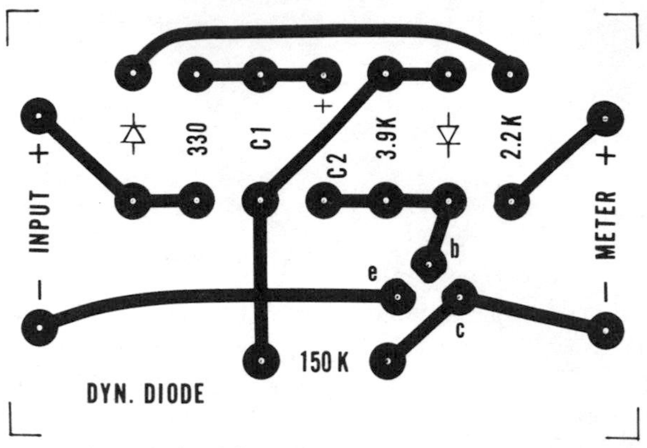

Fig. 7-5. The full-size printed-circuit board pattern.

nected in the proper polarity; reversed polarity prevents the meter from deflecting, even with a bad diode.

The printed-circuit pattern is shown in Fig. 7-5. Circuit tolerances are not critical, and neither is the transistor gain. The normal beta

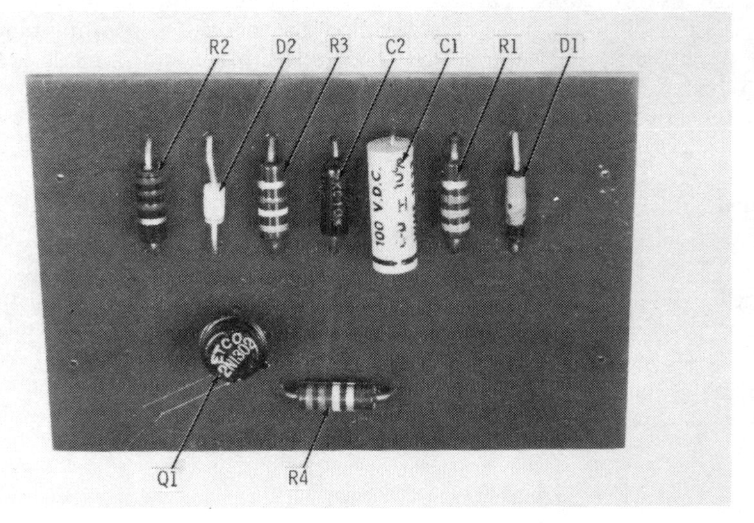

Fig. 7-6. A completed dynamic diode tester printed-circuit board.

range for the transistor specified (or its equivalent) is usually adequate. You can check the overall circuit function by connecting the input to 12 volts dc and bridging a 220K resistor between the positive input and the transistor base. This should cause from ¾ to off-scale meter deflection. See Fig. 7-6 for a completed dynamic diode

Table 7-1. Parts List for Dynamic Diode Tester

Item	Description
C1	Capacitor, .03 μF, 100 volts
C2	Capacitor, 1.0 μF, 35 volts, tantalum
D1, D2	Diode, silicon, 50 volts
M	Meter, 0–1 mA, 50-ohms internal resistance
R1	Resistor, 330 ohms, ½ watt, 10%
R2	Resistor, 2.2K, ½ watt, 10%
R3	Resistor, 3.9K, ½ watt, 10%
R4	Resistor, 150K, ½ watt, 10%
Q1	Transistor, npn, 2N1302, or equivalent

tester printed-circuit board. The parts list for the dynamic diode tester is given in Table 7-1.

USING THE DYNAMIC DIODE TESTER

It is very important that the test leads be connected directly to the alternator output terminal and ground. This is necessary to insure sufficient circuit resistance between the alternator and battery. Discharge the battery slightly before testing, as previously described. Then start the engine and quickly bring the speed up to about 1500 rpm or more while watching the meter. A little practice on several cars will show the response to expect. See Fig. 7-7 for a typical meter scale layout. It should be remembered that on cars having only a short connection between the alternator and battery, meter response will be less than with longer circuits. The effect of a shorted diode can be simulated by bringing out a short grounding wire from one of the diode pigtail connections in the alternator.

This test should always be made when testing an alternator charging system, even though the standard volt-amp tests seem normal. Abnormal test results will require that the alternator be removed for more detailed tests, as described in Chapter 14. In most cases an abnormal test will be caused by a defective diode. However, it is also possible for a defective stator winding to give the same meter reac-

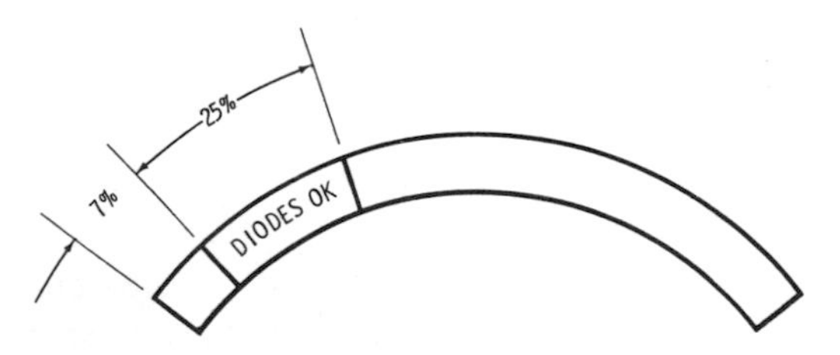

Fig. 7-7. A typical meter scale layout.

tion. This, of course, is detected by eliminating the diodes as the source of trouble. The dynamic diode test is not a substitute for the basic charging system tests but must be used in conjunction with them.

One final note on dynamic diode testing. If the circuit resistance between the alternator output terminal and the "hot" post of the battery is excessively high, the meter may indicate defective diodes even though they are good. Before removing the alternator, check this resistance with the volt-amp tester.

To do this, connect the volt-amp tester in the normal manner, and adjust engine speed to produce a 20-ampere charge rate. Be sure no other accessories are on. To get this charge rate, you may have to partially discharge the battery before testing. Then, using the 4-volt range, measure the voltage between the alternator output terminal and the "hot" post of the battery. If it is over 1 volt, there is excessive circuit resistance. Correct the cause and retest the diodes as before.

8

The Master Analyzer

The Master Analyzer is not a new instrument, but merely the combination of all the circuits described in Chapters 1 through 7. For the home builder it offers a number of advantages. First, of course, is economy; the cost advantage of only one meter and case is obvious. Second is the convenience of having all test functions available at the turn of a switch. Third, and perhaps most important to the builder, is the modular concept of construction. This permits you to build just the test circuits you feel are most necessary for your use. Each circuit is independent (except the tach, which shares the dwellmeter power source). You can start with one or two circuits and add others as time, money, and need warrant. When you finish, you will have an instrument comparable to professional units costing hundreds of dollars or more.

To aid you in this direction, we have supplied a full-size meter dial and panel layout. These can be reproduced and used "as is" or serve as a point of departure for your own creative design. Half the fun of making your own instruments is creating your own styling and packaging. Look at professional instruments for ideas, and then check local lumber and hardware stores for suitable construction materials. Don't overlook wood as a construction material. A well-designed wooden case, painted and accented with aluminum and wood-grained trim, makes a very attractive unit. If you prefer a ready-made case, the circuits fit nicely into a 7 × 10 × 8-inch metal utility cabinet (see Fig. 8-1).

You may also want to consider a stand for the completed instrument. This is not only a convenience but a form of insurance against dropping. Another approach is a wall-mounted, swing-out boom to hold the unit. This can be fashioned from standard water pipe and will practically eliminate any possibility of dropping.

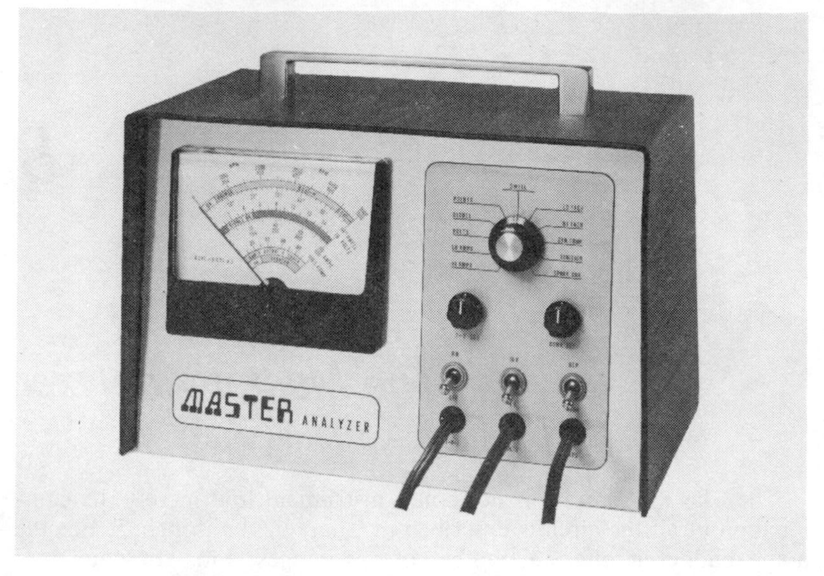

Fig. 8-1. A photograph of a completed Master Analyzer.

MASTER ANALYZER CONSTRUCTION

The heart of the analyzer is a 4-pole, 11-position rotary switch. This switches the meter and positive test lead to each of the individual printed-circuit boards. A block diagram of the complete instrument is shown in Fig. 8-2. Notice that only three sets of leads are used for all functions. The voltmeter and ammeter shunt leads are independent of the ignition leads. The volt-amp and dynamic diode printed-circuit boards are connected directly to the volt and amp leads and, except for the meter connections, do not go through the main test selector switch. However, they are connected to the voltmeter range and ammeter reverse switches. These switches, including the *on-off,* are toggle switches.

The tach and dwell circuits receive their power from a common battery supply adjusted with a 0–500-ohm set control. This consists of three size-D cells connected in series for 4.5 volts. When the dwell printed-circuit board is incorporated into the Master Analyzer, the 1.5K resistor must be changed to 2.7K. If this is not done, the tach will not calibrate properly. Also, connect a jumper between the R1 terminals. (The 1.5K resistor is used only when the dwell printed-circuit board is used in a single-function instrument containing a 3-volt source.) See Table 8-1 for the Master Analyzer parts list.

The individual printed-circuit board can be held in place by a wooden strip in which ⅛-inch deep saw cuts have been made. Space the cuts approximately 1 inch apart (1¼ inch for the dynamic compression printed-circuit board). A similar strip across the top securely clamps the printed-circuit board.

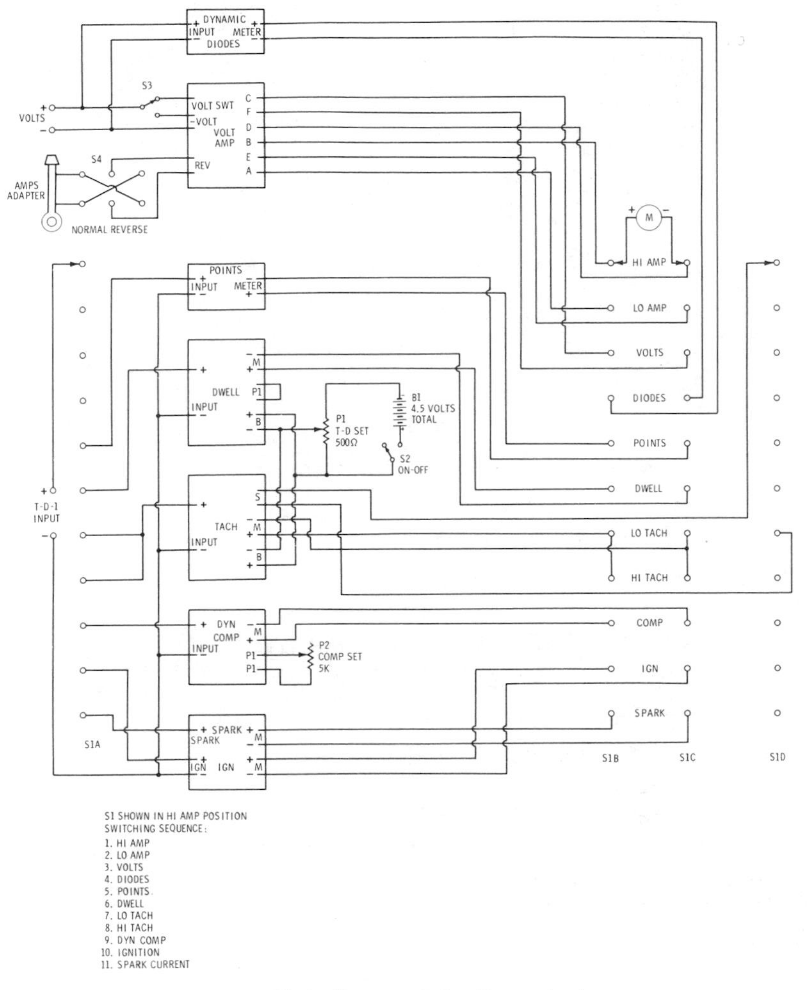

Fig. 8-2. Block diagram of the Master Analyzer.

The meter dial shown in Fig. 8-3 can be reproduced directly for use in a 4½-inch meter. It can be enlarged photographically for larger meters. To give a professional touch, the OK-BAD areas can be overlaid with a transparent colored film known as "Zip-A-Tone," available from art supply stores. Red, green, and yellow are the colors most commonly used.

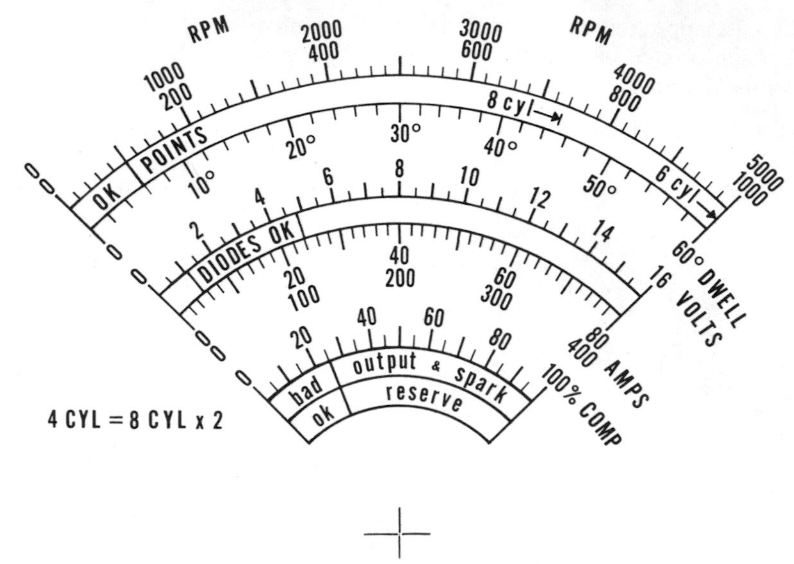

Fig. 8-3. Full-size meter dial.

The panel shown in Fig. 8-4 can also be reproduced full size. To protect it from abrasion and dirt, it can be covered with a thin Lucite sheet, which gives it an attractive appearance.

USING THE MASTER ANALYZER

Although the methods for using the various circuits have been covered in the previous chapters, there are a few details to observe. Both the tach and dwell are calibrated prior to use by turning to the DWELL

Table 8-1. Parts List for Master Analyzer

Item	Description
B1	Battery (3 size D cells)
M	Meter, 0–1 mA, 50-ohms internal resistance, 4½ inches
P1	Potentiometer, 500 ohms, wirewound (T-D set)
P2	Rheostat, 5K (compression set)
S1	Switch, rotary, 4 pole, 11 position (main selector)
S2	Switch, toggle, spst (on-off)
S3	Switch, toggle, spdt (4–16 volts)
S4	Switch, toggle, spdt (norm-reverse)
	Case
	Printed-circuit boards (see Chapters 1–7)
	Test leads
	Battery post adapter shunt (see Chapter 6)
	Three-cell battery holder

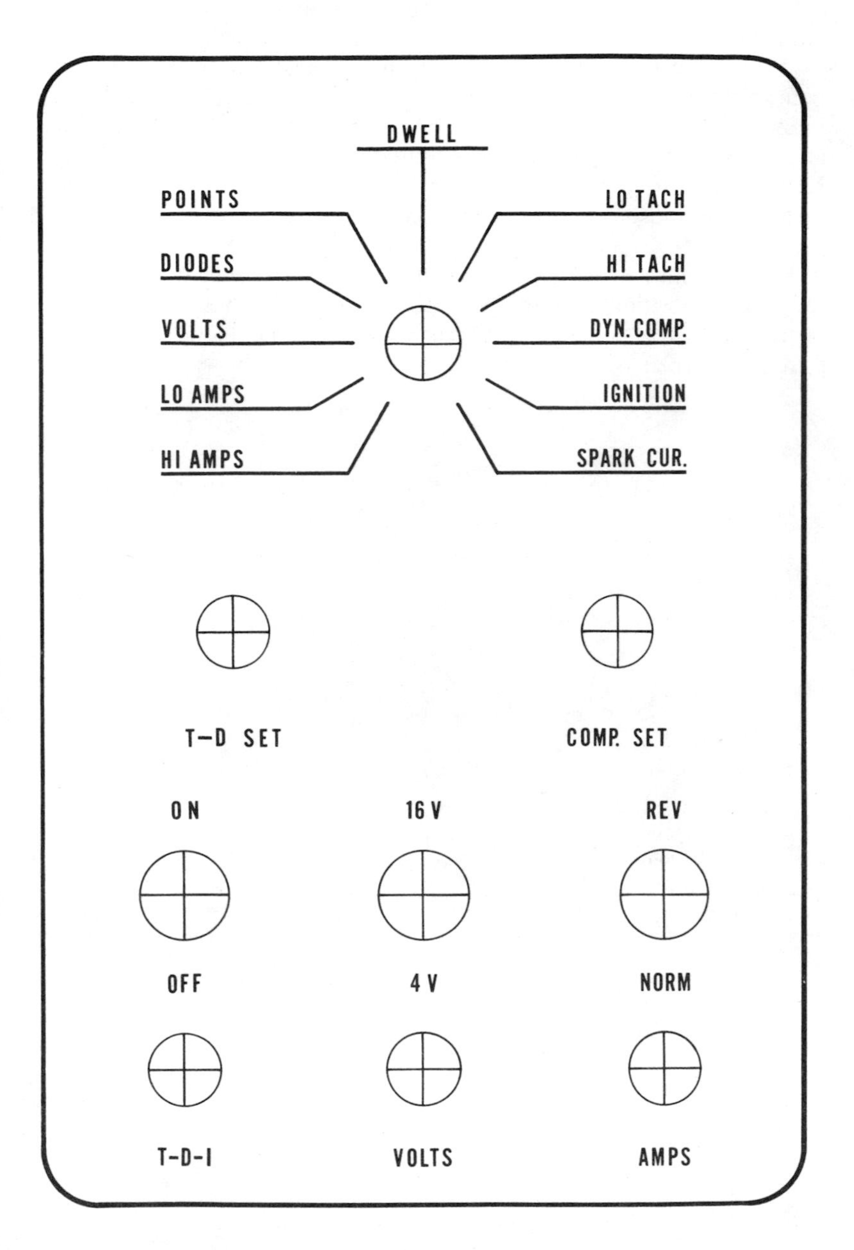

Fig. 8-4. Typical panel layout.

position and adjusting the T-D SET control to either the 8- or 6-cylinder marks. Be sure the test leads are disconnected at the time. Four-cylinder engines are tested by using the 8-cylinder setting and doubling the tach and dwell readings.

With the exception of the spark current test, all tach, dwell, and ignition tests are made with the T-D-I test leads connected across the points. All basic electrical system tests can be made with the volt and amp leads connected to the battery as described in Chapter 6. Remember, though, when making the dynamic diode test, the voltmeter leads must be connected to the alternator output terminal and ground.

For all routine tests, the ammeter reversing switch can be left in the NORM position and the voltmeter range switch in the 16-VOLT position. At the conclusion of tests, be sure the tach-dwell battery switch is turned off.

9

Building the Coil-Condenser Tester

In Chapter 4 we discussed various ways of testing the ignition system. Most of these tests were made on an operating ignition system. Sometimes, though, it is necessary to test a car that is not running or that will not start. For this test an ignition component tester, such as the coil and condenser tester described in this chapter, is quite handy. This instrument is especially helpful in troubleshooting the small engines used on lawnmowers, snowmobiles, minibikes and small motorcycles.

As we saw previously, coil troubles fall into three categories: shorted windings, open windings, and insulation breakdown. Open windings are easily detected with an ohmmeter. The one described in Chapter 14 is particularly useful for this purpose. An open primary winding, of course, causes complete loss of ignition. On the other hand, an open secondary winding is not immediately noticeable; the high-voltage spark can easily jump a small break in this winding. However, each time the spark jumps this gap, it burns away part of the wire. Eventually, the break is too wide for the spark to jump, and misfiring occurs. Any coil lacking secondary continuity (typically, 3–20K) should be replaced, even though it appears to function normally.

TYPES OF COIL TESTERS

Detecting shorted windings and insulation breakdown requires more specialized instruments. There are two types of coil testers being produced: the spark-gap type and the "Q" type. The spark-gap type simply shows whether the coil being tested, when driven with a fixed current, can produce a steady spark across a known gap. These testers are simple in construction and easy to use and will find most bad coils. They lack sensitivity on borderline coils—that is, coils in the early stages of failure that still operate normally under average conditions.

To find this kind of coil trouble, the "Q" type of tester is needed. The "Q" of a coil can be considered a measure of its efficiency. When a coil develops shorted windings, its "Q" is reduced considerably. There are a number of ways of measuring this factor. The one we will use is an adaptation of the ignition test circuit described in Chapter 4, since it is both simple and sensitive. As few as one shorted primary turn or thirty shorted secondary turns can be detected. It is also quite responsive to insulation breakdown, as we have already seen.

Actually, the instrument to be described is a combination of the spark-gap and "Q" type of coil tester. This approach eliminates the need for coil test specifications.

Since the condenser is so closely associated with the coil, most commercial coil testers also test this component. The more expensive instruments test a condenser for three conditions: series resistance, leakage resistance, and capacitance. Although these last two conditions can be tested with relatively simple circuitry, series resistance tests commonly involve some type of high-frequency oscillator (approximately 1 MHz). To eliminate the complexities of such a circuit, we will omit the series resistance test from our instrument and, instead, substitute a "master" condenser. The effect of high series resistance can be detected merely by paralleling this master condenser across the suspected component (see Chapter 3).

The other two factors, leakage and capacitance, cannot be measured by substitution. Paralleling a leaky or shorted condenser with a "master" condenser will not eliminate the problem. Capacitance, as we have seen, is important when diagnosing a condition of pitted points. By knowing condenser capacitance and applying the minus-minus-minus rule (Chapter 3), you will know what capacitance to use for replacement purposes.

BUILDING THE COIL TESTER

Because the coil testing function is independent of the condenser testing function, except for the common meter, we will treat them as two separate instruments. The coil tester is designed to work from a 12-volt battery. The circuit details are shown in Fig. 9-1.

The heart of this circuit is the vibrator, which simulates the action of the breaker points. Although these devices are becoming more rare, they are still easily available, especially from suppliers dealing in CB equipment. Another convenient source is old car radios. Most vibrators are made in either 3- or 4-prong versions; either type is suitable as long as it operates from 12 volts. Some are more efficient than

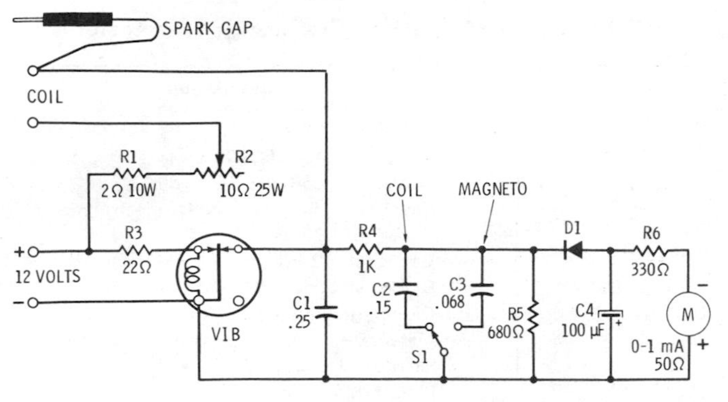

Fig. 9-1. The basic coil testing circuit.

others, so, if possible, check several. The two sets of contacts found in vibrators are called the "driven" set and the "rebound" set. So that the vibrator drive winding will not appear in the test circuit, we use the rebound contacts to operate the coil being tested. The capacitor connected across these contacts serves as the ignition condenser.

Rheostat R2 adjusts the coil primary current, which, in turn, controls coil output. The value of R2 is not critical, but it should be between 8 and 25 ohms and rated at 25 watts. Resistor R1 is a current limiter and should have a rating of at least 10 watts. The remainder of the circuit, the "Q" measuring portion, works on the same principle as the ignition test circuit of Chapter 4.

The purpose of the *coil-magneto* switch S1 is to alter the frequency response of the test circuit. The open circuit frequency of small flywheel magneto coils is typically 4–5 kHz, whereas conventional coils produce about 2–3 kHz. Some magneto coils will give sufficient deflection in the *coil* position, but most will require the *magneto* position. See Table 9-1 for the coil-condenser tester parts list.

The spark-gap assembly is an important part of the tester. Construction details are shown in Fig. 9-2. It actually serves as a high-voltage "voltmeter" to indicate when the coil is being driven enough

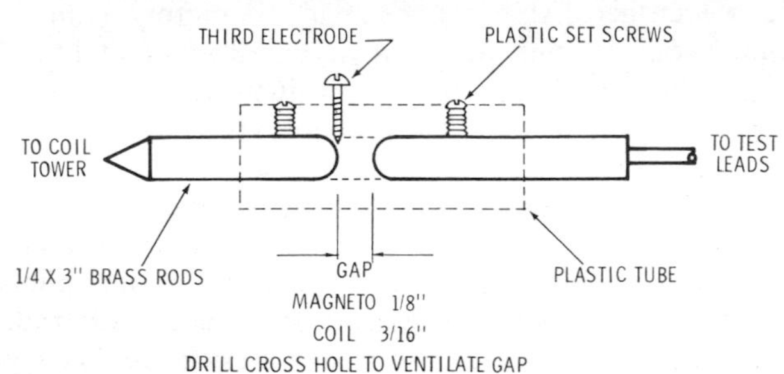

Fig. 9-2. An adjustable spark-gap probe.

Table 9-1. Parts List for Coil-Condenser Tester

Item	Description
C1	Capacitor, .25 μF, 400 volts
C2	Capacitor, .15 μF, 100 volts
C3	Capacitor, .068 μF, 100 volts
C4	Capacitor, 100 μF, 6 volts, electrolytic
C5, C6	Capacitor, .33 μF
C7	Capacitor, .2 μF
D1, D2, D3	Diode, silicon, 400 volts
D4 thru D7	Diode, germanium, 1N34 or equivalent
M	Meter, 0–1 mA, 50-ohms internal resistance
R1	Resistor, 2 ohms, 10 watts
R2	Rheostat, 10 ohms, 25 watts
R3	Resistor, 22 ohms, ½ watt, 10%
R4	Resistor, 1K, ½ watt, 10%
R5	Resistor, 680 ohms, ½ watt, 10%
R6	Resistor, 330 ohms, ½ watt, 10%
R7	Resistor, 220K, ½ watt, 10%
R8	Resistor, 1K, ½ watt, 10%
R9	Resistor, 1K, ½ watt, 10%
R10	Resistor, 4.9K, 2%
R11	Potentiometer, 500 ohms
S1	Switch, toggle, spdt
S2	Switch, rotary, 2-pole, 4-position
S3	Switch, toggle, dpdt
T1	Transformer, 125- and 6.3-volt secondaries
Vib	Vibrator, 3 or 4 prong, 12 volts

for test purposes. All coils share one thing in common: they must produce a certain minimum output voltage if they are to perform as ignition coils. Most automotive coils will produce a minimum of 20 kV. This gap is designed to fire between 14 and 18 kV, which means the coil will be sufficiently stressed to detect internal breakdown.

The most important part of this assembly is the shape and spacing of the spark gap. Radius the ends of the rods to a *smooth,* hemispherical shape. Use a drill bit as a gauge to get the proper gap. The "third electrode," which helps stabilize the spark, is merely a small machine screw pointed on the end. Screw it in to approximately .030 of an inch from the "hot" electrode. The screw just provides a slight capacitance effect. It makes no physical contact with the electrodes.

ADDING A CONDENSER TESTER

The condenser testing section is ac operated, as shown in Fig. 9-3. Transformer T1 provides not only the low voltage for the capacitance measuring circuit but isolation from the line. Capacitance is determined by measuring capacitive reactance at 60 Hz. As the capacitance increases, its reactance decreases, causing increased meter current. The meter is scaled directly in μF. It is calibrated, prior to use, by clipping the leads together and adjusting R11 for full-scale meter deflection.

Although condenser leakage could be measured with a conventional service *vom,* it lacks sufficient voltage for a valid test. An ignition condenser is subjected to voltage as high as 300 to 400 volts. To simulate this condition, the leakage test circuit should provide voltages of this magnitude. The circuit of Fig. 9-3 utilizes a voltage doubler to produce a potential of 300 volts dc. The condenser under test is connected across this voltage, via the meter and R7. Any leakage resistance will cause a deflection of the meter. Normally, a good condenser will have no detectable leakage; however, a condenser is still serviceable down to 5 megohms of resistance. Since this test does not require high precision, no circuit calibration is needed.

The 300-volt potential is not dangerous since current is limited by R7. The charge put on the condenser being tested, though, can give you a shock if it is not bled off after testing. This is accomplished automatically (resistor R8 acts as a bleeder) when the test selector switch is returned to the OFF position.

The "master" condenser C7 is not critical in value; therefore, any good ignition condenser can be used.

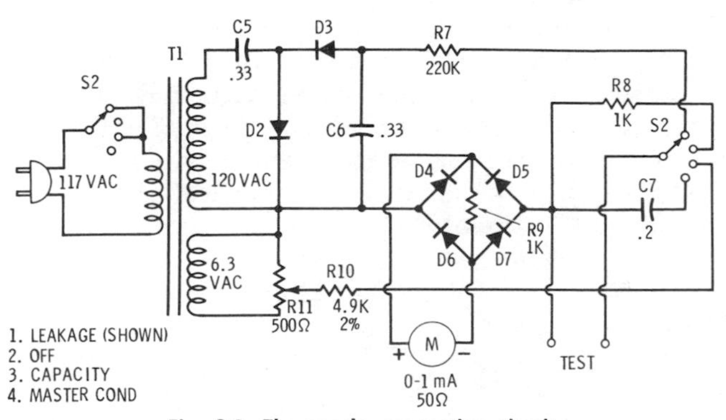

Fig. 9-3. The condenser testing circuit.

A COMBINATION COIL-CONDENSER TESTER

By combining the coil and condenser testing functions in one instrument, you can make one meter serve for both circuits. A block diagram for such a combination is shown in Fig. 9-4. The dpdt toggle switch S3 provides an easy way of switching the meter, although this could be incorporated into the test selector S2. No switching, other than the S1 *coil-magneto* switch, is needed in the coil test cir-

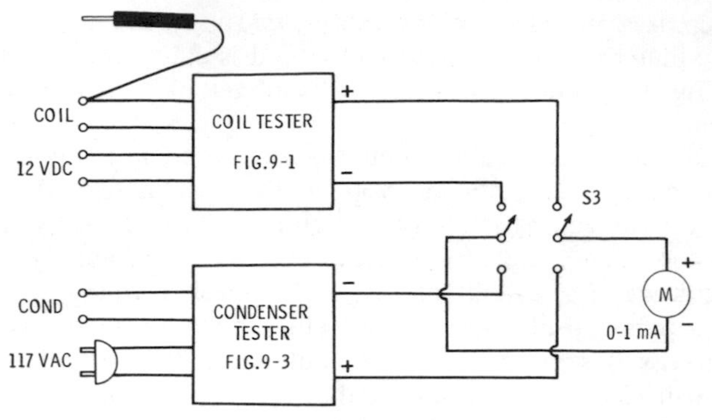

Fig. 9-4. A combined coil-condenser tester.

cuit. A full-size meter dial suitable for most 3½ inch, 100° meters is illustrated in Fig. 9-5.

USING THE COIL-CONDENSER TESTER

A coil can be tested either in or out of the car. If it is being tested while still in the car, be sure to disconnect the two primary wires and remove the high-tension wire from the coil tower. Connect the battery leads, observing polarity. Connect the test leads to the coil primary terminals and install the spark gap in the coil tower.

As the input control R2 is gradually turned up, the meter should start to show increased deflection. Continue turning R2 until the spark-gap just begins to fire; the meter should be reading in the GOOD band (on some coils it may be reading off-scale). Turning the control up further for a steady spark should cause the meter reading to drop into the BAD band. This is the normal reaction of a good coil.

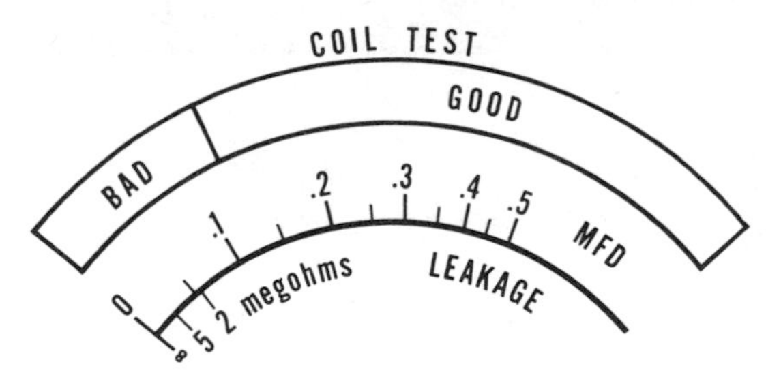

Fig. 9-5. Full-size dial for 3½-inch meter.

If the meter shows only slight or zero deflection as coil current is increased, it indicates a shorted coil. Likewise, an open primary winding produces no meter deflection. If the reading increases normally but drops back before the spark-gap fires, it indicates internal coil breakdown. If the reading increases normally but the spark is erratic or nonexistent, it indicates a possible open secondary winding. Check this by measuring the coil secondary resistance. It is possible for a coil with only one or two shorted primary turns to produce an apparently normal spark, although there will be virtually no meter deflection. Such a coil will, of course, function normally under normal driving conditions but may cause misfiring during the high ignition demands of acceleration.

Flywheel magneto coils, like those found on small engines, can also be tested, either installed or removed. If they are still installed, be sure the breaker points are open and the kill switch, if so equipped. If the coil is removed for testing, keep in mind that some of these have a secondary winding that is not connected to the primary winding. In these cases, connect a short jumper between one of the secondary windings and one of the primary windings before testing.

When testing these magneto coils, connect across the primary winding and follow the same basic procedure as for conventional coils. Because of their lower output, use a ⅛-inch spark gap. Adjust the input control to produce steady sparking (this may not be quite as steady as that of a regular coil), and then lift off the spark-gap. The meter should read in the GOOD band, but on some small coils it may read close to the BAD band. Remember, it is not the amount of meter reading that determines the coil quality, but, rather, the fact that the meter *does* deflect.

USING THE CONDENSER TESTER

When you test condensers, be sure the pigtail lead is disconnected. There is no polarity to the condenser tester leads. After testing capacitance and leakage, return the test selector to the OFF position to discharge the condenser before removing the test leads.

THE MASTER CONDENSER

The master condenser serves one purpose: to take the place of a suspected open or high series resistant condenser. Merely connect the test leads across the points of the engine being tested. If there is an improvement in starting or running, a defective condenser is indicated. On small engines with flywheel magneto systems, you can frequently make this connection between the "kill" switch and engine ground. These switches normally parallel the points and condenser.

OTHER USES FOR THE CONDENSER TESTER

In addition to condenser tests, the leakage test function can be used for other purposes. Since it is actually an ohmmeter, it can be used to check the continuity of a coil's secondary winding. Because of its high potential, it can also be used to detect leakage in other electrical components, such as the rotor or stator windings of alternators or the armatures of starters and generators. Normally, these

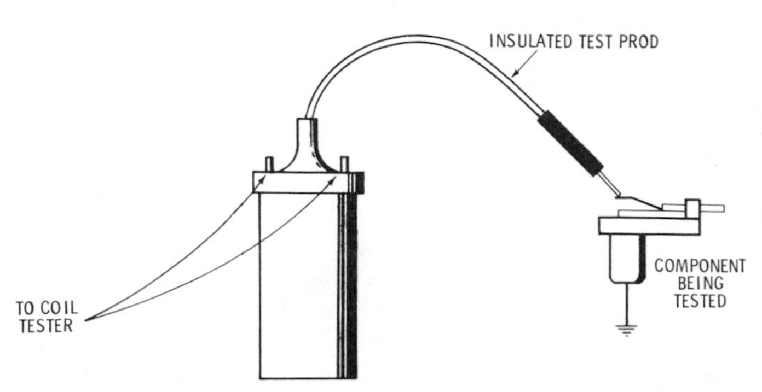

Fig. 9-6. High-voltage testing of a rotor (or other ignition component).

windings should be completely insulated from ground and, therefore, should show no leakage. Although the presence of a moderate amount of leakage would not affect operation, it can indicate the possibility of a future short circuit. The leakage circuit should not be used to test alternator diodes; disconnect them before testing the insulation of alternator stator windings.

OTHER USES FOR THE COIL TESTER

The coil tester also finds use in many of the electronic ignition systems now appearing on an increasing number of cars. A number of these systems use a conventional ignition coil that is activated either by a transistor switch (instead of the points) or a capacitor discharge circuit. These coils can be tested in the same manner as those in conventional systems. Follow the same procedure, but be sure the coil is completely disconnected from the ignition system.

Another handy application is high-voltage testing of the cap, plug wires, and rotor. While this can be done with the ignition test circuit of Chapter 4, it requires a running engine. If this is neither practical nor possible, use the coil being tested as a source of high voltage to test the insulation of the other ignition components. (See Fig. 9-6.) If there is no insulation breakdown in the part being tested, there will be no drop in the meter reading.

10

The Mini-Analyzer

The Mini-Analyzer is a compact, easily-built tester that fulfills a number of needs for the automotive enthusiast. For some, the Mini-Analyzer is just the right size of tester; it covers all the basic test functions without involving much cost or construction time.

Even for those who have built the Master Analyzer of Chapter 8, this little instrument has its place. It would be the perfect "take along" tester. As your reputation for being able to troubleshoot and diagnose automotive problems spreads, you will be frequently asked ". . . what do you think might be the trouble with my car?" A few basic checks with the Mini-Analyzer can usually narrow the trouble area down to a few possibilities. Also, it gives a comforting thought, on a long trip, to know that you have the means of doing some troubleshooting in an emergency. With the Mini-Analyzer and a few hand tools you can solve many of those unexpected problems that seem to come up far from home.

One final argument for the Mini-Analyzer. Once word gets around that you have automotive test instruments, there will be the usual borrowers. The Mini-Analyzer is the perfect instrument to lend. It can withstand improper usage and is virtually goof-proof. This saves your more sophisticated instruments for the one person who truly appreciates them—you.

The Mini-Analyzer is a combination tach-dwell and volt-amp tester. The unit described in this chapter is quite basic in its functions and ranges, but it can be readily modified to meet almost any particular requirement. We have covered the fundamental design principles for the various test functions in other chapters. If you wish to modify the following circuit, refer to the appropriate chapter.

SELF-POWERED TACH

The tach range reads from 0 to 2500 rpm. This is a compromise range but one that will cover approximately 90% of routine testing requirements. Unlike the previously described tachs, this circuit is self-powered. It does not require an internal battery, which is advantageous in several ways. It cannot be accidentally left on and does not require any pretest calibration. On the other hand, it also has a disadvantage. The power to operate the tach circuit must come from the ignition system under test. This means that it has a higher loading effect on the ignition system than does the previously described transistorized circuit. As a result, its use is generally confined to conventional-type ignition systems. It may not function on some of the more specialized ignition systems, such as capacitor discharge or transistorized systems.

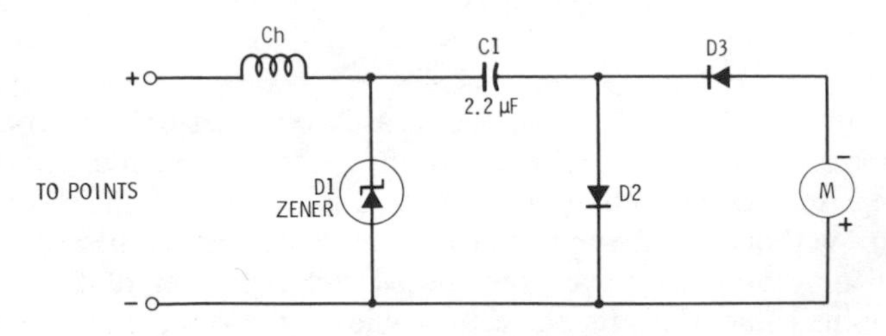

Fig. 10-1. A self-powered tach circuit.

The principle of the self-powered tach circuit is similar to the transistorized tach circuit. That is, it relies on the charging of a capacitor from a fixed potential and then discharging that capacitor through a meter. This switching action is accomplished by diodes as shown in Fig. 10-1.

When the breaker points open, the ignition primary waveform appears across the input circuit. The choke presents a relatively high impedance to the high frequency, high voltage pulses present in this waveform. The zener diode clamps this voltage to approximately the level of the zener voltage. This is the voltage that charges the charge capacitor. The charging current, however, passes through diode D2 and is prevented from going through the meter by diode D3. The charge placed on the capacitor is held there until the breaker points close.

When the points close, this charged capacitor is effectively connected across the meter (via the points). The polarity of the charged capacitor is such that it will now discharge through diode D3 and the meter, causing the usual up-scale deflection. The amount of deflection is determined by the value of the capacitor, zener voltage, and meter sensitivity. In fact, the same tach design formula shown previously applies to the self-powered circuit.

It will be apparent from the circuit operation that since the capacitor discharge current passes through the breaker points, poor point action will affect the meter response. With normal points, this effect is not noticeable, but bad points can cause a slight meter error or unsteady reading. This is one reason why this circuit is seldom used in more expensive instruments. However, considering the purpose for which this unit is designed, this fact is offset by the independence from internal batteries.

SELF-POWERED DWELL

The dwell function is simplicity itself. The same choke-zener input is used. The meter is merely connected, through a fixed and variable resistor, across the zener diode. There is no capacitor in this circuit (Fig. 10-2). When the points are closed, the voltage across the zener is zero (disregarding the normally slight voltage drop across the points). When the points are open, the zener clamps the battery-ignition voltage to approximately 5 volts (the zener voltage). The meter receives, alternately, either 0 or 5 volts; the latter is the voltage required to give full-scale deflection. The meter responds to the *average* voltage level, which is directly proportional to the dwell period (see Chapter 1 for more details). The result is that the meter deflection is directly proportional to the percentage of dwell. However, this deflection is the opposite of a standard dwellmeter. One hundred percent of dwell is at the left end of the meter scale, and zero is at the right.

A single range, 0–250-amp ammeter scale is used. This one range allows you to test both charging and starter systems. Although this somewhat limits scale resolution for charging system tests, you can still measure to better than 5 amperes—more than adequate for all basic tests. Polarity reversal is incorporated into the main test selector switch.

The ammeter is designed around the battery post adapter shunt shown in Fig. 10-3. This is similar to the one used in Chapter 6 and

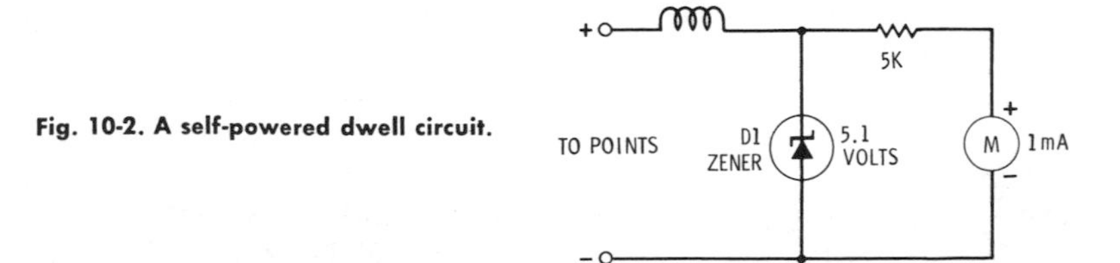

Fig. 10-2. A self-powered dwell circuit.

can be made from readily obtainable materials. Since the temperature coefficient of the steel in the shunt is about the same as that of the copper in the meter, the ammeter will remain reasonably accurate over a wide range of temperatures.

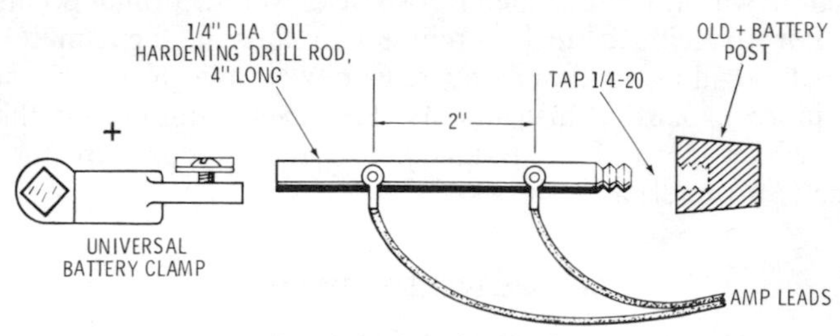

Fig. 10-3. The adapter shunt.

CIRCUIT CONSTRUCTION

The circuit details are shown in Fig. 10-4. The most important component is input choke Ch. For best results this should be an air-core type. An iron-core type can cause dwell inaccuracies at higher speeds, although it will have no effect on the tach circuit. The inductance can vary from 50 to 100 millihenries with a dc resistance between 140 and 475 ohms, preferably about 200 ohms. Zener D1 should be a ½- to 1-watt type at approximately 5.1 volts to match the recommended capacitance of 2.2 μF for C1. The voltage rating of this capacitor can be as low as 10 volts. If you use a tantalum (recommended type) capacitor, install it in the polarity shown. Diodes D2 and D3 are general purpose germanium types.

The voltmeter multiplier R1 can be a precision 1% unit or a hand-selected combination of 10% resistors. The proper value for this resistor is indicated by the meter showing the correct reading when connected to a known voltage (see Chapter 6 for one way of checking a voltmeter). All other circuits are calibrated by the adjustable resistors, R3 through R6, described under calibration. See Table 10-1 for the Mini-Analyzer parts list.

The circuit is simple enough that it can be hand-wired, or you can use the full-size printed-circuit pattern shown in Fig. 10-5. The lowercase letters shown on the pattern refer to the corresponding letters in the schematic to help in wiring the board to the switches. Two switches are required: a spdt toggle switch for the 6- and 8-cylinder tach selector and a 3- (or 4-) pole, 5-position rotary switch for the test selector. A completed printed-circuit board of the Mini-Analyzer is shown in Fig. 10-6.

Any 0–1 milliamp meter having a resistance of 80 ohms or less can be used. If the resistance is greater, it will be necessary to make

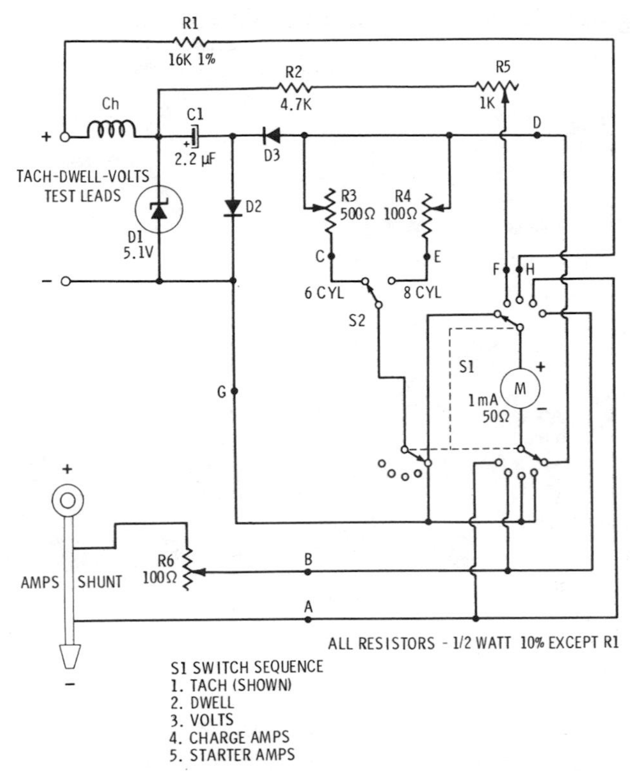

Fig. 10-4. The Mini-Analyzer circuit.

Table 10-1. Parts List for Mini-Analyzer

Item	Description
C1	Capacitor, 2.2 μF, 10%, 10-volt minimum, tantalum or equivalent
Ch	Choke, 50–100 millihenry, air core, Miller 994 or equivalent
D1	Diode, zener, 5.1 volts, ½–1 watt
D2, D3	Diode, germanium, 1N34 or equivalent
M	Meter, 0–1 mA, 50-ohms internal resistance
R1	Resistor, 16K, ½ watt, 1% (or hand-selected combination)
R2	Resistor, 4.7K, ½ watt, 10%
R3	Rheostat, 500 ohms, CTS Type 115 or equivalent
R4, R6	Rheostat, 100 ohms, CTS Type 115 or equivalent
R5	Rheostat, 1K, CTS Type 115 or equivalent
S1	Switch, rotary, 3-pole, 5-position
S2	Switch, toggle, spdt
Misc	3 × 4-inch PC board, 18-gauge twin conductor for test and shunt leads, test clips, switch knob, case and panel. See Fig. 10-3 for shunt details.

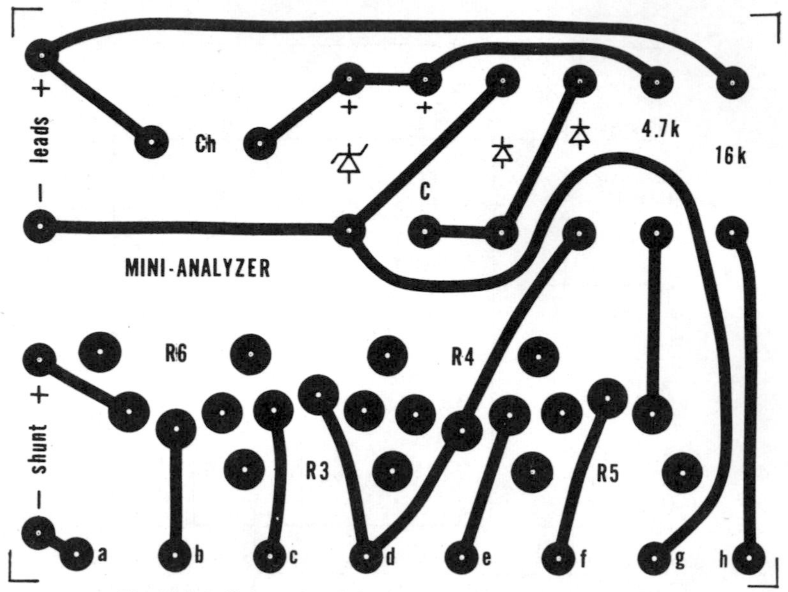

Fig. 10-5. Full-size printed-circuit pattern for the Mini-Analyzer.

the shunt somewhat longer to provide calibration range for the ammeter. The suggested meter dial shown in Fig. 10-7 can be reproduced directly to fit most 3½″, 100° meters, or it can be enlarged photographically to fit larger meters.

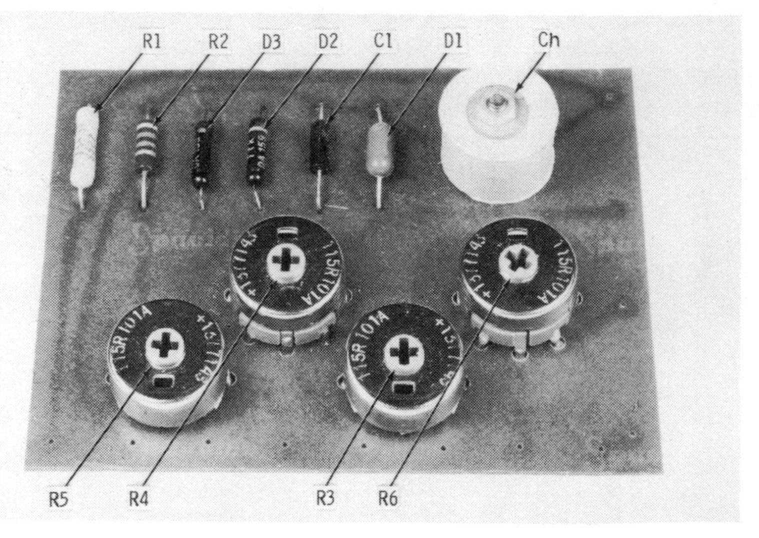

Fig. 10-6. A completed printed-circuit board for the Mini-Analyzer.

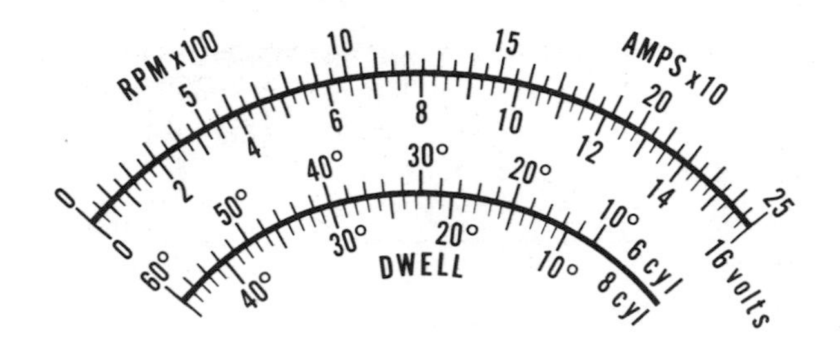

Fig. 10-7. The meter dial.

CALIBRATION

The dwell range is calibrated simply by connecting the test leads to a 12-volt battery, setting the switch to DWELL, and adjusting R5 for full-scale meter deflection. The tach range can be calibrated by using the test set-up in Fig. 10-8. Transformer output should be between 10 and 15 volts ac. Any 0.5 amp silicon diode can be used, but the 50-ohm resistor should be at least 3 watts. Connect the test leads across the 50-ohm resistor, observing polarity, and set the switches to the TACH and 6-CYL. positions. Adjust R3 to give a meter reading of 1200 rpm. Set the switch to the 8-CYLINDER position and adjust R4 to give a reading of 900 rpm. This completes the tach and dwell calibration.

The voltmeter calibration has been previously described. The best way of calibrating the ammeter is by comparison with a known accurate ammeter. If such an ammeter is not available, a reasonably close calibration can be made using 100 feet of 14-gauge copper wire as a load resistor. The solid wire used for house wiring is inexpensive and works well for this purpose. This gives a resistance of .25 ohm, which, when connected across a 12-volt battery, will draw 44 to 48 amperes. This must be done quickly, as the copper wire will heat up and change its resistance. Assuming a constant .25 ohm, the cur-

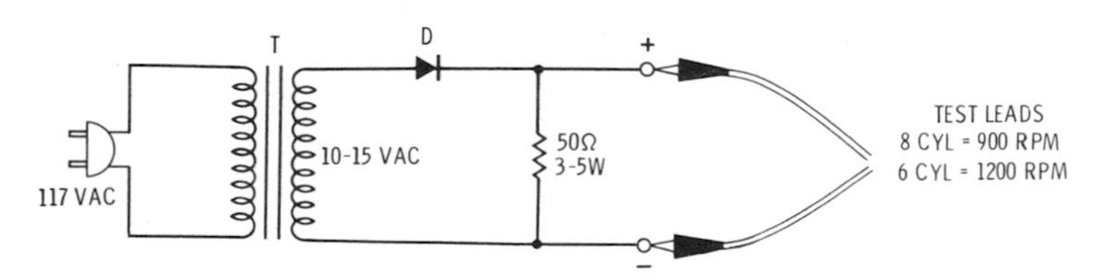

Fig. 10-8. Tach calibration circuit.

rent in amperes will equal four times the battery voltage under this load. Adjust the ammeter control R6 to give this reading. See Fig. 10-9. The test selector should be in the STARTER position; the CHARGE position should give a reverse meter reading.

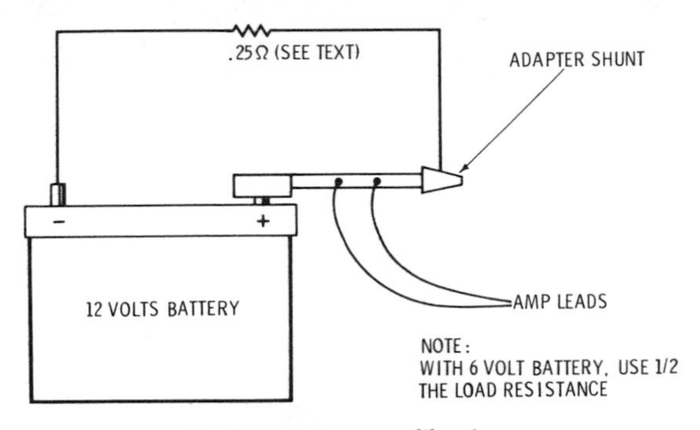

Fig. 10-9. Ammeter calibration.

USING THE MINI-ANALYZER

In spite of its simplicity, the Mini-Analyzer is capable of many tests. Most of these have been described in other chapters and can be readily applied to this instrument. However, the following procedures will show its basic applications.

Connections

1. Remove the positive battery clamp, and connect the adapter shunt between the battery post and the disconnected cable.
2. Connect the test leads directly across the battery terminals.

Starter Test

1. Pull the high-tension wire from the coil to prevent starting.
2. Set the test selector to the STARTER position.
3. Crank the engine and note the starter current drain on the 0–25 scale. (Multiply reading by 10.)

Battery Test

1. Set test selector to VOLTS position.
2. Crank engine and note cranking voltage reading on 0–16 scale. The voltage should not drop below 9.6 volts (4.8 for 6-volt batteries) if battery is serviceable.

Generator/Alternator Output Test

1. Crank engine without starting for about 10 seconds to partially discharge battery. Then, reconnect coil wire.

2. Set test selector to CHARGE position.
3. Start engine and immediately increase speed to approximately 1500 rpm or higher, while watching 0–25 scale. The highest reading before the pointer starts to fall back is the alternator output in amperes (multiply reading by 10). On a generator system, this will be the current regulator setting. Add 5 amps for ignition current.

Charging Voltage Test

1. Continue operating engine at a fast idle until ammeter reading drops back to 10–15 amperes. (If charge rate remains high, battery is probably discharged.)
2. Set test selector to VOLTS position.
3. With engine at approximately 1500 rpm, note voltage reading. This is the charging voltage at the battery and will be within a few tenths of a volt of the actual voltage regulator setting.

Dwell Test

1. Connect the test leads across the ignition breaker points: red or positive to coil primary terminal and black or negative to engine ground (reverse for positive ground).
2. Set test selector to DWELL position and note dwell reading at idle on appropriate scale. For 4-cylinder engines, use the 8-cylinder range and double the readings.

Dwell Variation Test

1. Increase speed to 1500 rpm and note change, if any, in the dwell reading. See Chapter 1 for detailed explanation.

Engine Speed Measurements

1. Set test selector to TACH position and the switch to the proper cylinder position. The reading on the 0–25 scale times 100 is the engine speed in rpm.
2. For 4-cylinder measurements, use the 8-cylinder position and double the meter readings.

11

Automotive Timing Lights

Engine timing is one of the most important steps in tune-up. Consider what happens when timing is late or retarded: the engine loses power, gas mileage and, in extreme cases, can even overheat. On the other hand, timing that is too advanced also wastes power by causing knock and ping. Because of the extreme combustion pressures involved, considerable damage can be done to the pistons. This knocking and pinging of too advanced timing, though, is quite noticeable; as a result, we are aware of it and correct it. It is the more common problem of retarded timing that most frequently goes unnoticed.

But there is much more to timing than just making an initial adjustment. In this chapter we will look at various aspects of engine timing and the ways and means of testing and adjusting it.

Engine timing falls into two categories. The first and most familiar is the setting of the initial timing. This is the basic, but not the only, purpose of the timing light. The second is the timing of the engine under all combinations of speed and load. This is the function of the distributor advance mechanisms. Although the home mechanic may not have the special equipment for calibrating these mechanisms, he can at least check their performance. Now consider the role these advance mechanisms play in the overall timing of the engine.

MECHANICAL ADVANCE MECHANISMS

Most distributors contain two separate timing advance mechanisms (Fig. 11-1): (1) the mechanical advance unit and (2) the vacuum advance unit. The mechanical advance unit is directly coupled to the distributor drive shaft and responds only to shaft or engine speed. The mechanical advance controls ignition timing for all engine speeds above idle. Because a given air-fuel mixture tends to burn at a constant rate, it must be ignited earlier and earlier as engine speed increases, if it is to complete its burning at the proper point in the power stroke.

The mechanical advance mechanism is not unlike a governor. As speed increases, weights, acting against spring tension, start to move out by centrifugal force. This outward movement causes a slight shift or advancement of the distributor cam, which causes the points to open sooner. The amount by which the timing should advance at any particular speed is determined by the mechanical advance curve. This is usually given in terms of "distributor degrees advance versus distributor rpm" or "engine degrees advance versus engine rpm." This latter specification is always twice the former because of the 2:1 ratio between engine and distributor speed.

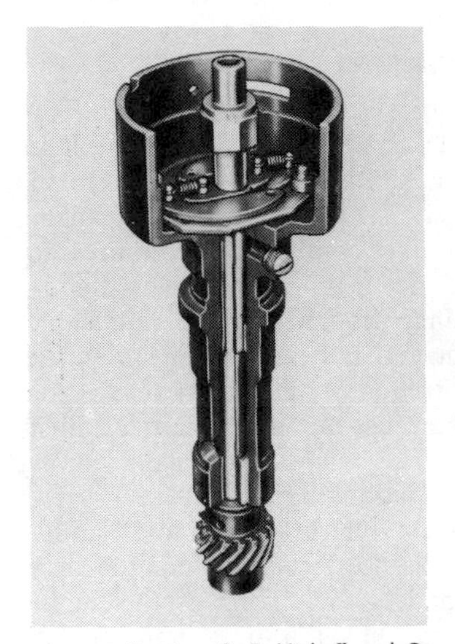

Courtesy C. E. Niehoff and Co.

Fig. 11-1. A mechanical advance mechanism.

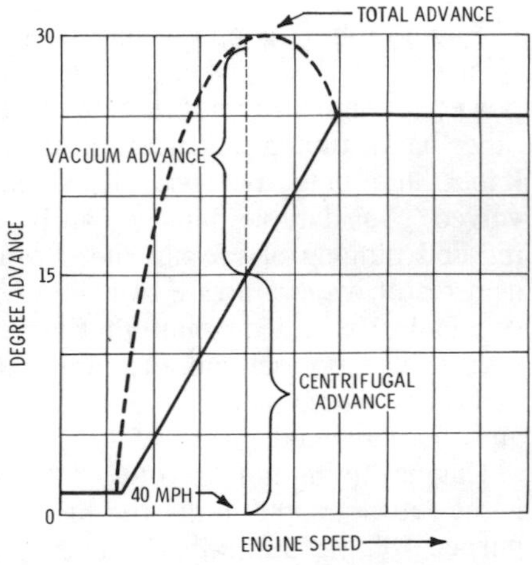

Courtesy C. E. Niehoff and Co.

Fig. 11-2. Typical mechanical and vacuum advance curves.

THE VACUUM ADVANCE UNIT

The vacuum advance unit also advances ignition timing, but for a different reason. While mechanical advance controls engine timing on the basis of *speed,* vacuum advance controls timing on the basis of engine *load.* Vacuum advance is always in addition to mechanical advance. At a given speed, the engine is under some degree of load. When the load is heavy, no additional advance (other than that provided by the mechanical advance) is required. But as the load decreases, as under level cruising conditions, the air-fuel mixture becomes leaner (and slower burning) and requires additional ignition advance. Typical mechanical and vacuum advance curves are shown in Fig. 11-2.

Engine load is reflected in the amount of vacuum existing in the intake manifold. By feeding this vacuum back to the vacuum advance unit (Fig. 11-3), it will vary engine timing in proportion to engine load. When the load is heavy, such as during acceleration, the vacuum is low or nonexistent. Under these conditions no additional advance is added. But under light load cruising conditions the vacuum is high, and the full vacuum advance is added to the mechanical advance.

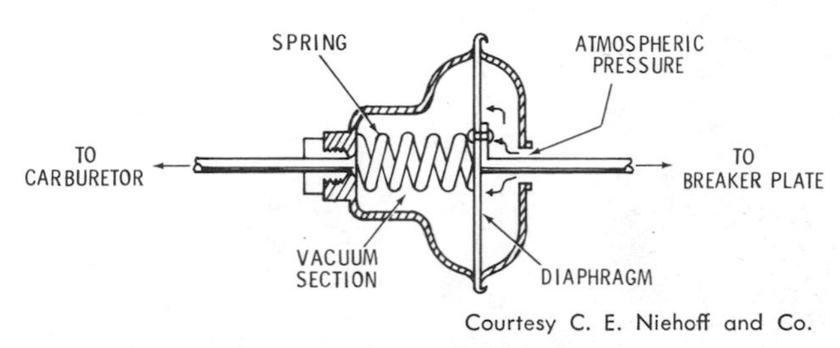

Courtesy C. E. Niehoff and Co.

Fig. 11-3. How a vacuum advance works.

We can generalize the functions of the two advance mechanisms and say that the mechanical advance controls the performance (acceleration and power) of the engine, while vacuum advance controls the economy (gas mileage) of the engine. A faulty vacuum advance is not always immediately noticed, since it does not affect acceleration. It should also be noted that both advance mechanisms will be off by whatever amount the initial timing is off. Initial timing cannot compensate for improper advance. At the end of this chapter we will discuss the setting of initial timing and the checking of the advance mechanisms.

Until recently, certain Ford engines used a distributor advance mechanism operated solely by vacuum. This vacuum was determined by both engine speed and load. In effect, this device combined the functions of the mechanical and vacuum advance in a single unit. Testing these units requires equipment normally not available to the home mechanic.

ENGINE TIMING METHODS

An engine can be timed two ways: (1) statically or (2) dynamically. Static timing is the older method and is still used for certain engines. As the name implies, it is done with the engine stopped. The first step is to rotate the crankshaft to the firing position for the number one cylinder. This is generally shown by the alignment of a timing mark with a fixed pointer (Fig. 11-4). The distributor is then loosened and turned slightly until the points just open. The opening can be detected by turning on the ignition and connecting a voltmeter or test light across the points. Unless you use care, backlash in the distributor shaft can cause timing errors.

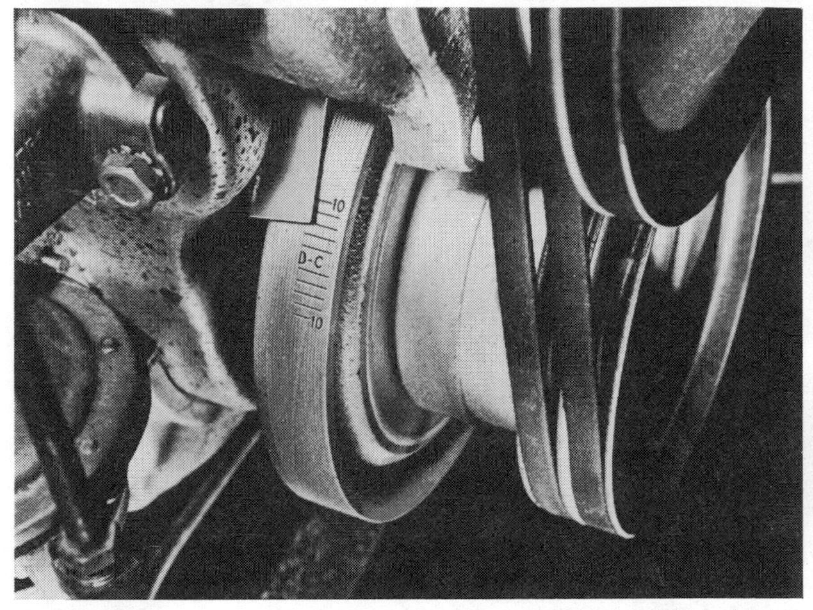

Courtesy C. E. Niehoff and Co.

Fig. 11-4. A common timing mark location.

The static method is occasionally used when an engine is badly out-of-time or is being reassembled after an overhaul. This sets the timing close enough so the engine can be started and then precisely timed dynamically. Dynamic timing is done stroboscopically with the engine running. The earliest stroboscopic timing lights used a neon-filled flash tube. This was connected in series with the number one plug lead. When this plug fired, the tube would flash and momentarily "freeze" the motion of the flywheel or vibration damper. The operator could continuously monitor the position of the timing mark to the fixed pointer as he made his adjustments. These inexpensive neon lights are still available, but they suffer from two defects: their light output is very low, and they do not completely "freeze" the motion. Timing has to be carried out under almost dark conditions. Because the flash tube stays on for the duration of the spark current, the timing mark moves through an appreciable distance and tends to blur the image.

POWER TIMING LIGHT

Both of these shortcomings were overcome with the development of the power timing light. The light output of this device is derived not from the spark current, but from a separate, high-voltage power supply. A xenon-filled flash tube replaces the neon tube and gives a high-intensity white light of short duration. The timing light is still connected to the number one plug, but the firing of that plug serves merely to trigger the flash tube. A block diagram of a typical power timing light is shown in Fig. 11-5.

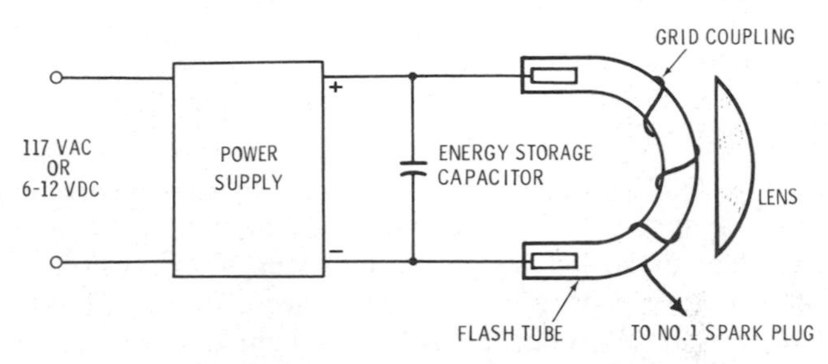

Fig. 11-5. The major parts of a power timing light.

The power supply delivers anywhere from 300 to 500 volts dc. This charges an energy storage capacitor that is connected across the flash tube. The flash tube has an external grid or coupling winding, which is connected to the number one plug. The time constant of the power supply and storage capacitor is such that it can recharge the capacitor between the successive firings of the plug. This is no problem for lights designed for low-speed timing applications, but it must be considered in high-speed light design. A time constant also exists between the storage capacitor and flash tube. It should be kept as short as possible by using a capacitor with low internal resistance. Excessive resistance delays the discharging of the capacitor, thus extending the duration of flash and reducing the apparent light output.

The power supply can be either ac or dc operated. Ac operation results in an economical and dependable circuit but generally restricts the light to in-shop use. A dc light, on the other hand, can be used anywhere, since it derives its power from the car's own battery. However, it must be compatible with both 6- and 12-volt systems if it is to function on all cars. Most commercially built lights are designed this way.

There are two important factors to consider in building either an ac- or dc-operated timing light. These are the power supply voltage and the capacitance of the storage capacitor. Together, they determine the energy delivered to the flash tube and, hence, the light output.

For low-speed work, a relatively bright light is desired because of the low repetition rate of the flash. For higher-speed work, a lower light output can be used. Although the light output is proportional to the energy stored in the capacitor, the *apparent* light output does not increase in direct proportion. In other words, a point is reached where increasing the energy does not result in an appreciable increase in apparent light output.

The relationship between light output, power supply voltage, and storage capacitance is shown in the following formula.

$$J = \frac{1}{2} CE^2$$

where,

J is the energy delivered to tube (watt-seconds),
C is the storage capacitance in farads,
E is the power supply voltage.

Notice that the light energy varies directly with the capacitance of the storage capacitor, and by the square of the voltage. For this reason, most commercial lights operate between 300 and 500 volts dc. The typical storage capacitor is on the order of 2 μF. This seems to be a good compromise between sufficient light output and longevity. Higher light output not only puts a heavier load on the power supply, but also reduces the life of the flash tube.

Flash tube triggering is accomplished by the external grid. Various ways of doing this are possible. The easiest is merely to wrap a few turns of bare wire around the tube, somewhere between the electrodes. The winding is adjusted or spaced to provide the proper "coupling." This determines the level of spark plug voltage at which the flash tube fires. It is not always possible to obtain a perfect adjustment. If the coupling is made sensitive (i.e., the grid windings spread apart) to work on a car with low sparking voltages, it may be too sensitive on another car with high sparking voltages. This is evidenced by the flash tube being triggered from the induced voltage of other plugs as well as the plug to which it is connected. Although this does not affect the ability of the light to time an engine, it is annoying.

On the other hand, setting the coupling for minimum sensitivity (i.e., grid windings close together) may result in missed flashes. This too is undesirable. The best setting for the grid coupling is a compromise. Slight overcoupling or undercoupling, as extra or missed flashes are called, is not serious. You will also find that as the flash tube ages, its triggering requirements tend to increase. When the tube flashes erratically, even with maximum coupling, it should be replaced. The triggering level also varies with the supply voltage; flash tubes are more sensitive with higher anode voltages.

Thus far we have considered only the electrical requirements of timing lights. The light of the flash tube must be focused to be effective. This is accomplished by a short-focal length, condenser-type lens placed close to the tube to focus the flash about 12 inches away. Because the entire flash tube cannot be in the same focal plane of the lens, exact focusing is not possible.

AN AC-POWERED TIMING LIGHT

Ac-powered lights are easy and inexpensive to build and are well-suited for home construction. Because they are ac-operated, the builder should take every precaution to insure adequate insulation. If you work on both 6- and 12-volt cars, an ac light may be preferable to a dc light. Ac lights are equally bright on cars of all voltages—a feature not always obtained even with commercial dc lights.

In this type of circuit you have a choice of two kinds of power supply: (1) a voltage doubler circuit or (2) a transformer operated circuit. From a performance standpoint, there is little difference between the two. The voltage doubler circuit is the least expensive and is typical of most commercial ac units. The supply voltage is limited to about 300 volts dc. This tends to limit the light output, but it is sufficient for all ordinary applications. A doubler circuit has the advantage of compactness, which makes packaging the light quite easy. The entire circuit can be readily contained in a 1½-inch diameter plastic tube. A typical circuit is shown in Fig. 11-6.

You have some leeway in the choice of capacitors, depending on the intended use of the light. The energy storage capacitor C2 is the most important and the most critical. It should be a high quality capacitor to assure minimum internal resistance. Only a few ohms of internal resistance can reduce the light output by half. Generally, this capacitor is of a mylar or paper type; an electrolytic type can be used, provided it exhibits minimum series resistance.

The usual range of this capacitor is between 2 and 6 μF, with a rating of 350 volts or more. The higher value should be restricted to low-speed lights used primarily for ignition timing. Although it gives a good, bright light, it tends to shorten tube life and, at high speeds,

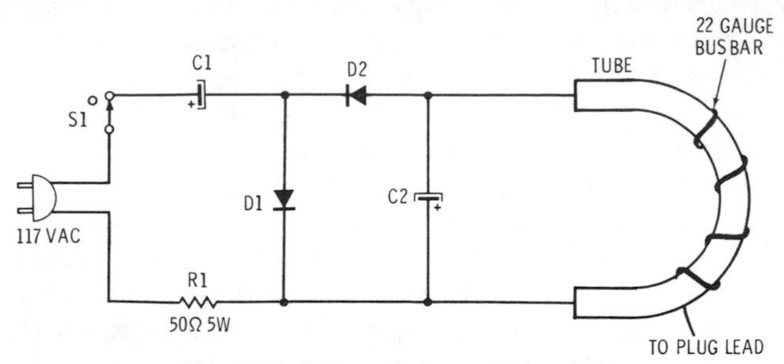

Fig. 11-6. A home-built ac timing light.

can cause the tube to overheat. A value of 2 μF gives a reasonably bright light and is better suited to high-speed use, such as advance testing at 2500 rpm or higher. Actually, because of the high flash rate, there is little advantage to a large capacitor at high speeds.

Capacitor C2, which can be a 350-volt electrolytic, is generally equal to or slightly larger than the storage capacitor. By use of a circuit trick, you can use a large storage capacitor for bright, low-speed timing without unduly straining the tube at higher speeds. If C1 is 2 μF and C2 is 6 μF, the flash tube will operate at full voltage at low idle speed. At higher speeds, the high flash rate does not permit C2 to charge to full voltage, since C1 is smaller than C2. The actual light output per flash is less, but the *apparent* light output remains about the same. However, this does mean that the flash tube is operating below its normal voltage, which could cause triggering irregularities.

Diodes D1 and D2 are 1-amp, 400-volt silicon devices. Resistor R1 serves as a current limiter for the diodes. The momentary contact switch S1 effectively eliminates unnecessary flashing. See Table 11-1 for the ac timing light parts list.

Table 11-1. Parts List for AC Timing Light

Item	Description
C1	See text
C2	See text
D1, D2	Diode, silicon, 400 volts, 1 amp
R1	Resistor, 50 ohms, 5 watt, wirewound
S1	Switch, toggle, spdt, normally open (push button)
Flash tube	Amglo Type U-35 or replacement tube for ac timing lights
Line cord	18 ga twin conductor
Spark plug lead	High voltage test prod wire
Misc	Plastic or fiber tube for housing, short focal length condenser lens

Flash tubes (such as the Amglo Type U-35) are available from electronic parts companies. They can also be obtained as replacement tubes for the timing lights sold by mail order companies or automotive parts distributors. The two anode leads of the tube should be well soldered to capacitor C2. The peak currents in this part of the circuit are quite high and cannot tolerate poor connections. Wrap a few turns of bare busbar wire around the tube for the triggering coupling. Use heavily insulated test prod wire between this trigger coupling and the spark plug connector. A handy spark plug adapter, which can be permanently attached to the trigger lead, is shown in Fig. 11-7.

A focusing lens completes the basic elements of the light. The choice will be influenced by the size of the holder containing the flash tube and other parts. These lenses have very short focal lengths (a thick lens) and are usually about 1¼ to 1¾ inches in diameter. They need not be (and generally are not) of a high quality. Lenses used

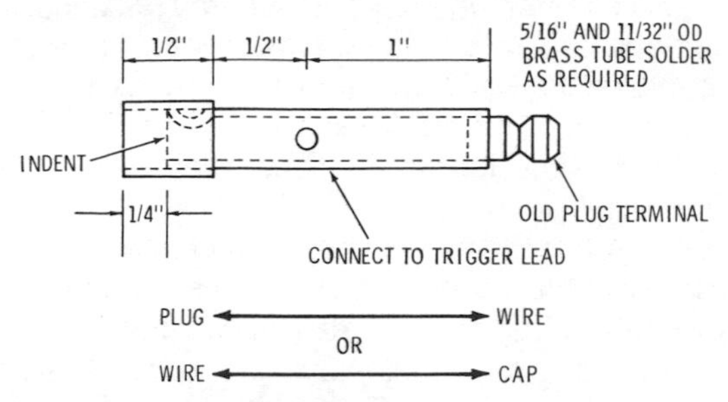

Fig. 11-7. A universal timing light connector.

as condensers in projectors work especially well and can be obtained from science supply companies for a reasonable price. Position the lens close to the flash tube and adjust it to give the best spread of light at about 12 inches.

DC-POWERED TIMING LIGHTS

For a light that can be used anywhere, you can substitute a dc inverter for the ac doubler circuit described above. Transformers for

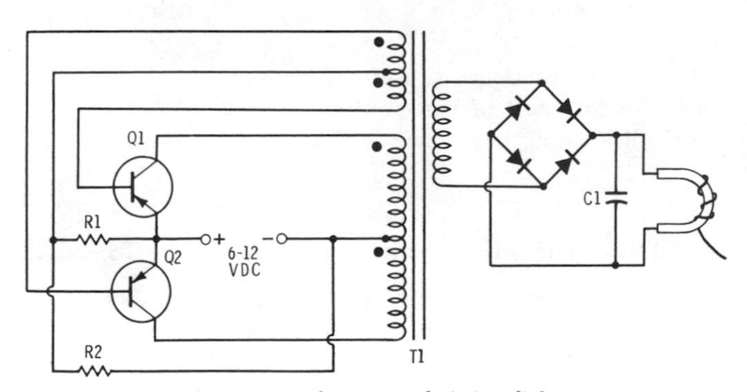

Fig. 11-8. A dc powered timing light.

these circuits are usually custom wound to keep their size to a minimum. For this reason, specific circuit details cannot be given. A typical circuit is shown in Fig. 11-8. If you have access to the proper cores, toroidal transformers are not too difficult to hand wind. Circuit details are available from the component manufacturers.

SETTING IGNITION TIMING

Setting timing is deceptively simple. But if you observe a few rules, you will have no problems. First, be sure the dwell is properly set *before* timing the engine. Changing dwell after setting timing alters the timing by the amount of the dwell change. Second, always disconnect the distributor vacuum line. This is a precautionary measure to ensure that the vacuum advance unit is inoperative, which is especially important on cars timed at speeds above idle. Should it be partially advanced during timing, the actual timing will be late by the amount of the partial advance.

Connect the trigger pick-up to the number one spark plug. Normally, this will be the cylinder closest to the radiator. If in doubt, check a service manual. You can also make this connection at the distributor; the number one plug wire is frequently marked with a red cap. Operate the engine at the specified timing speed. In most cases, this will be the normal idling speed. If the engine is running too fast during timing, the mechanical advance may start to function, causing a timing error as described for the vacuum advance unit. Some cars, on the other hand, *must* be timed at specified speeds *above* idle.

Timing is effected by rotating the distributor housing to bring the timing mark and pointer into alignment. Be sure to recheck timing after tightening the distributor mounting clamp.

Timing can always be checked from two spark plugs: the number one plug and the first plug in the second half of the firing order. (However, this is *not true* with Volkswagens.) For example, a 6-cylinder engine, which has a 1, 5, 3, 6, 2, 4 firing order, can be timed from either the number 1 or number 6 spark plug. This fact provides for a quick check of distributor shaft alignment or cam wear. If the timing does not check the same on both plugs, a misalignment or wear exists.

CHECKING THE MECHANICAL ADVANCE MECHANISM

There is little the home mechanic can do to precisely measure the advance curve. Fortunately, the mechanical advance mechanism is quite reliable and seldom gives much trouble. However, several checks can be made that do not require special equipment. One is simply a mechanical check to see if the mechanism is free to move and not sticky. To do this, grasp the rotor and twist it in the direction of its normal rotation. You should be able to feel the tension of the advance weight springs. When released, the rotor should snap back to its original position. Practice this on several cars to get the proper feel.

Another check involves more effort but may be worthwhile when tracking down an elusive performance problem. From the distributor advance data determine the number of *engine degrees of mechanical advance* at 2000 or 2500 engine rpm. At this point disregard data for total or vacuum advance. After measuring the diameter of the pulley containing the timing mark, calculate the distance from this mark to the specified advance point. See Fig. 11-9.

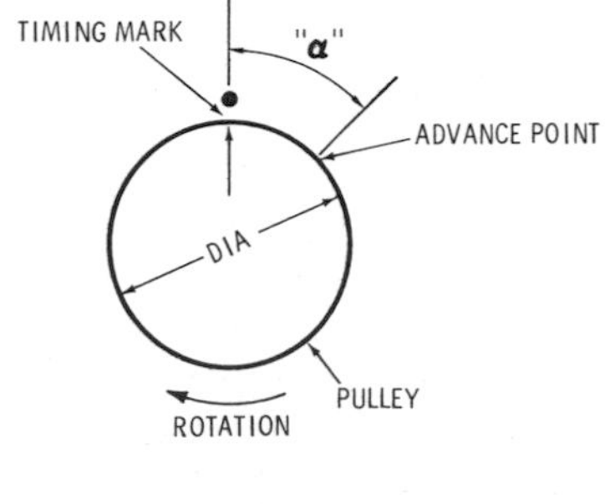

Fig. 11-9. Marking the pulley to measure distributor advance.

$$\text{"}a\text{"} = \frac{\text{ENGINE DEGREES ADVANCE} \times \text{DIA} \times 3.14}{360}$$

Use a strip of paper cut to length "a" to transfer this distance to the pulley. Be sure to measure from the specified ignition timing mark and not from the tdc (top dead center) mark, unless the engine is timed at tdc. Also, be sure to disconnect the distributor vacuum line before making this test (and take care to connect it again after the test). Using the timing light, set the initial timing as specified. Then increase engine rpm to the specified test speed with the timing light directed at the pulley. If the advance mechanism is working properly, the advance point will appear under the fixed timing mark.

Knowing how the vacuum advance unit operates, we can check its performance much as we did the mechanical advance. Since the vacuum pick-up point is normally above the idle position of the throttle, this test must be made well above idle speed. The additional total advance of the vacuum unit can be added to the pulley as before. While testing the mechanical advance, merely reconnect the distributor vacuum line and note the additional shift of the mark.

12

Testing With the Oscilloscope

One of the first commercial automotive scope analyzers appeared in England shortly after World War II. It was what we now call a "primary" scope (to be discussed later), and was designed for use by automotive mechanics. Previously, such scopes had been confined to laboratory use by design engineers. This was the forerunner of many automotive service scopes, which first began appearing in garages and service stations during the 1950's.

The automotive scope is basically an ignition analyzer. This fact is not always realized by many potential operators. There is a tendency to look upon the automotive oscilloscope as an electronic "crystal ball" that can plumb the innermost workings of an engine. Unfortunately, this is not the case. In fact, once you find out what scope analysis is all about, the automotive scope becomes quite a commonplace instrument.

This immediately raises several questions: what is the real value of an automotive scope and can a scope do things that standard meter instruments cannot do?

SCOPE VERSUS METERED INSTRUMENT

Anyone who has used a scope for general electronic testing knows that it has one major advantage over a metered instrument; it shows an instantaneous picture of what is happening. Actually, it creates a graph, usually voltage versus time, on the face of the cathode ray tube (crt). A metered instrument generally shows only an average value—*average* coil voltage, for instance, or *average* dwell angle.

The scope could well be called "the universal ignition analyzer." Merely by moving your eye, you can quickly analyze a number of ignition conditions that would have required almost as many metered test circuits. The two advantages of the scope are it does the work of three or four separate testers and does it very quickly.

If the reader thinks he has wasted his time building metered instruments when he should have concentrated on a scope, let's put the scope in its proper perspective. First, good automotive scopes are expensive. As we mentioned, their chief asset is rapidity of testing. For the average hobbyist, this is no advantage when he considers the cost. For the busy commercial shop, though, success of the business depends on time saved in analysis.

Second, with one or two exceptions, there is little a scope can do that cannot be done by properly designed metered instruments, except to do it faster. This will become more clear as we go through an actual scope analysis. In fact, there are some areas in which meters not only do as well, but actually perform better than a scope. For example, a scope *can* measure dwell, but for all practical purposes, this can be best accomplished with a standard dwellmeter.

One purpose of this chapter is to show the reader just what can and cannot be done with a scope in automotive testing. We will do this by adapting a standard, general-purpose oscilloscope to the ignition system. This way, the reader can explore all facets of scope testing and decide for himself his own need for an ignition scope. The serious experimenter will no doubt add such an instrument to his collection. The average hobbyist may well decide that his metered instruments answer all his testing requirements.

SCOPE OPERATION

The secret of using a scope hinges on waveform analysis. It makes little difference whether you are using an elaborate, commercially built automotive scope or a jury-rigged hobby scope; the waveforms and their analyses are the same. Originally, scope analysis was done by the "picture book" method. The operator was furnished a virtual catalog of all possible waveform variations with their attendant ignition faults. This proved cumbersome to use.

The present method is much quicker and is a true analytical approach. Before going into the actual analysis, the reader should be cautioned against "over-reading" the pattern or waveform. Over-reading means attaching unwarranted significance to insignificant portions of the pattern. This is a natural tendency of beginners, especially if they have had no previous scope experience. A certain amount of "hash" is always present in the ignition waveform; most of it is meaningless for our purposes.

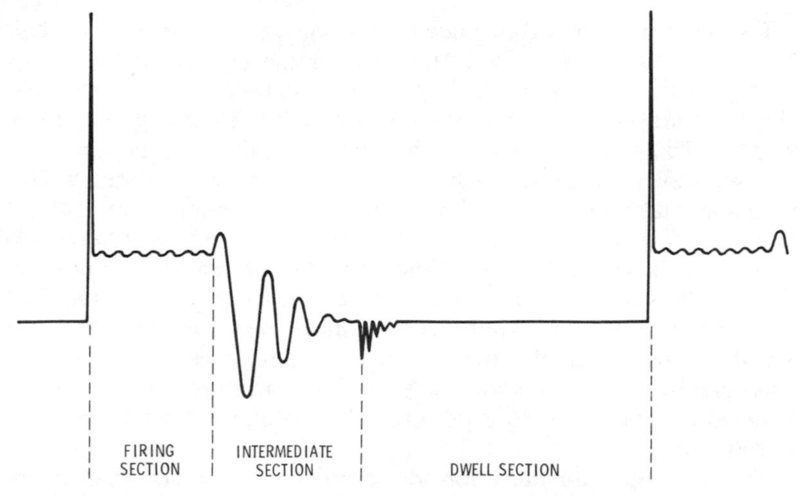

Fig. 12-1. The ignition secondary waveform.

IGNITION WAVEFORMS

The whole concept of ignition waveform analysis is shown in Fig. 12-1. This is called the ignition secondary waveform and covers the complete ignition cycle for one cylinder. Ignition scopes can be adjusted to show just the one pattern for each cylinder or to show all cylinders simultaneously. Each method has its purpose. Some scopes also show a primary pattern, which we will discuss later.

Notice that the pattern in Fig. 12-1 has been divided into three sections. Each section pertains to a particular phase of the ignition cycle and has its own qualities. These sections are relatively independent of each other; a particular ignition fault will show up in one section but not in another. The three sections are called:

1. The firing section.
2. The intermediate section.
3. The dwell section.

First, we will examine the firing section (Fig. 12-2). It is composed of two components: the vertical "firing line" and the horizontal "spark line." The firing line indicates the amount of voltage required to break down or fire the spark plug. It is sometimes called the ionization voltage. The higher the firing line, the higher the firing voltage. Once the spark plug gap breaks down, or fires, the spark voltage falls to a much lower value. This is shown by the level of the spark line. The voltage across the plug gap remains at this level until the spark extinguishes at the end of the spark line. This completes the firing section of the pattern. Now, analyze these two lines.

To understand the significance of the firing line requires an understanding of how a plug fires. In order for the coil voltage to jump the gap of the spark plug, the gap must first become ionized. Actually, there are two gaps that must be ionized: the rotor gap and the plug gap. The plug gap, however, has the predominant influence.

The coil voltage must reach a certain level before ionization and breakdown take place. This level depends on a number of factors, namely compression pressure, air-fuel ratio, engine temperature, spark plug gap, and shape. A lean air-fuel mixture, for example, requires a higher firing voltage than a rich mixture. High compression requires more voltage than low compression. A major factor is the shape and gap of the spark plug electrodes. Worn or rounded electrodes require considerably higher breakdown potential than do new or sharp-cornered electrodes. Wide gaps, naturally, require more voltage than narrow gaps.

The scope operator must consider a number of factors when interpreting the firing line. Frequently, the results of a scope analysis must be correlated with other test data to arrive at a proper diagnosis. For instance, low compression and/or rich mixtures, both of which lower the firing voltage, could mask or offset the high firing voltage of a worn plug. A scope analysis by itself is not always the final answer.

The spark line, the more or less horizontal component of the firing section, is somewhat easier to interpret. This part of the ignition cycle occurs after the plug gap has broken down. It could be called "the voltage required to maintain the spark." When the bulk of the coil energy has dissipated itself across the plug gap, the voltage becomes insufficient to maintain the spark. The spark then extinguishes.

The spark line is not influenced by as many factors as the firing line. Aside from the plug itself, the major influence is the amount of

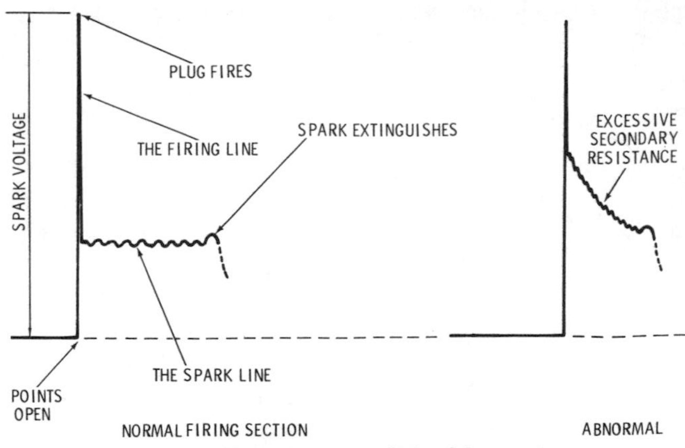

Fig. 12-2. The main parts of the firing section.

resistance in the high-tension circuit. This includes the spark plug wire, which is generally a resistance or suppressor type wire, and any other part of this circuit that may contain resistance. Many scope users consider the spark line a test of the suppressor resistance normally built into the plug wires or rotor. Typically, this resistance is on the order of 5 to 25,000 ohms and has little effect on the spark line. But when it deteriorates and becomes excessively high (which eventually causes ignition misfiring), the spark line becomes noticeably higher and can develop a considerable slope. When this kind of trouble occurs, it is usually restricted to a few plug wires. It shows up readily when all cylinder patterns are compared as a group.

DWELL WAVEFORMS

We will temporarily skip the second section of the pattern and go, instead, to the dwell section. The purpose of this section is quite apparent. It begins with the points-close signal (Fig. 12-3) and ends with the points-open signal. The duration of this section is the dwell period. Many scopes have a scale printed on the scope graticule to permit a direct measurement of this line in degrees of dwell.

Normally, it is easier to measure dwell with a dwellmeter. For one particular dwell test, however, the scope has an advantage. With the scope it is possible to measure the dwell of each individual cam lobe. Theoretically, each cam lobe should have the same amount of dwell. If the cam wears unevenly, different lobes will have different amounts of dwell. This has the effect of altering the timing to certain cylinders, even though the number one cylinder is properly timed. This does not show up on the dwellmeter, since it shows only average dwell, but it does show up on the scope.

This section shows the action of the breaker points and the dwell measurement. If you have provisions for making high-speed dynamometer or road tests, it will detect point bounce. This shows up as

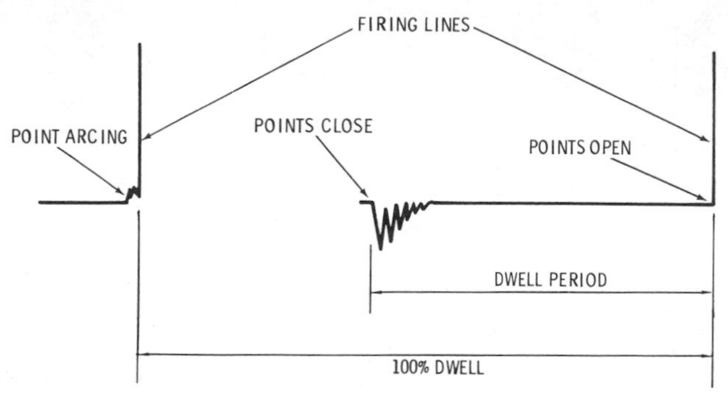

Fig. 12-3. The dwell section.

a false firing line shortly after the points-close signal. At lower speeds it can indicate poor contact condition. This is shown by an erratic signal at the points-close portion. Actually, the dynamic points resistance test (see Chapters 3 and 14) is more sensitive than the scope for this purpose. Arc-over during the opening of the points is shown at the points-open signal. This appears as a jagged step on the following firing line. Such a condition could be caused by excessive dwell or an open (or high-resistance) condenser in the distributor.

INTERMEDIATE WAVEFORMS

Now we shall return to the second or intermediate section of the pattern. This was saved for last because it is a "residual" section. In other words, whatever part of the ignition cycle that is not used up by either the firing section or the dwell section goes to the intermediate section. This fact confuses many beginners, but its explanation is quite simple.

The interval of time allotted to any ignition cycle, that is, the interval between one firing line and the next, is determined by the speed of the engine—the higher the speed, the shorter the interval. A fixed percentage of this interval is taken up by the dwell section. This depends on the dwell angle and is independent of speed. The firing section also takes a certain amount of time. This is the length of time it takes for the coil to dissipate its energy at the plug gap and is relatively independent of engine speed. The time interval for the firing section remains fairly constant, so as the speed goes up and the time between ignition cycles becomes shorter, the dwell section runs into the firing section. The intermediate section is simply squeezed out of the pattern.

Thus, the intermediate section must be observed at lower speeds, such as idle or up to about 1000 rpm. In fact, it is possible that there will not be an intermediate section, even at idle speed. If the dwell

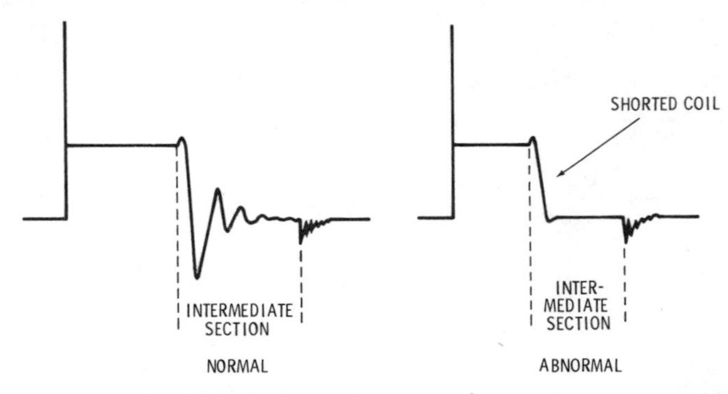

Fig. 12-4. Analyzing the intermediate section.

Fig. 12-5. A primary pickup adapter.

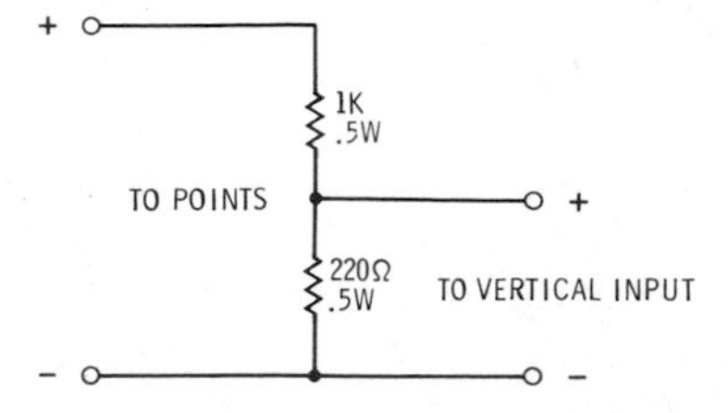

angle is unusually high, which can occur with dual-point distributors, the dwell section will run into the firing section, eliminating the intermediate section altogether.

The intermediate section is frequently called the "coil and condenser" section. Its purpose is to indicate any shorted windings in the coil. Normally, the intermediate section appears as a series of damped sine waves, caused by the dissipation of the remaining energy in the coil. If the coil has shorted windings, either in the primary or secondary, these sine waves will be virtually nonexistent. See Fig. 12-4.

USING YOUR OWN SCOPE FOR IGNITION ANALYSIS

Most general purpose service scopes can be used for ignition analysis with suitable adapters. They are not as convenient to use as scopes designed specifically for this application, since they usually lack a triggered sweep. The lack of this sweep makes it more difficult to lock in the waveforms, but with proper syncing it can be accomplished. Since speed of connection and adjustment are not important for our needs, this is no problem.

Two types of waveforms are observed with an ignition scope: primary and secondary. Two types of signal pickups are required. The first is a simple resistive divider for primary waveform observation, as shown in Fig. 12-5. The other is a secondary or high tension pickup and is shown in Fig. 12-6. Most commercial ignition scopes use only

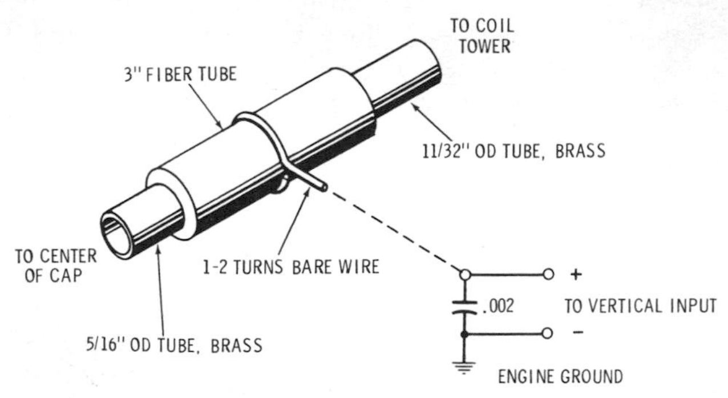

Fig. 12-6. The secondary pattern pickup.

a secondary pickup. Actually, most of the ignition troubles detectable with a scope show up in both waveforms. The secondary pickup is necessary for plug voltage measurements and shows better the effect of secondary resistance. However, since we will not have a calibrated secondary pickup, we can measure only relative voltage levels.

The secondary pickup is basically a low-value, high-voltage capacitor that can be readily connected into the high-tension circuit. This forms a capacitive divider with the suggested .002-μF capacitor, as illustrated in Fig. 12-6. You may have to alter these values to suit your particular instrument. The best pickups are frequency-compensated RC voltage dividers, but they are seldom found. The suggested pickup can be made from the thin-wall brass tubing found in hobby shops. A heavy-walled fiber tube provides the insulation, and a single turn or two of bare wire forms the other plate of the capacitor.

TROUBLESHOOTING

To localize ignition troubles to a particular cylinder, all waveforms are referenced to the number one cylinder. In a commercial scope, the trigger pickup would be connected to the spark plug of this cylinder. In our application we will make a loose capacitive coupling by wrapping a few turns of wire around this plug lead and feeding the wire back to the sync input of the scope.

Before we begin the actual analysis with our makeshift connection, it is helpful to know a trick used by all commercial scope manufacturers. The waveforms you see on your scope will most likely be inverted from those shown in the illustrations or those you would see on a commercial scope. The secondary pattern is normally a negative-going waveform, and your scope shows it in its true polarity. Commercial scope makers reverse this pattern to make it easier to interpret (increasing voltage goes up, not down). An opposite, or positive-going pattern, usually means that the ignition coil is connected backwards.

The secondary pickup is installed in the center tower of the distributor cap, with the coil wire plugged into the other end. Connect the sync coupling as previously described, and you are ready to begin. Operate the engine at about 1000 rpm and adjust the sweep rate to show one waveform for each cylinder. You may lose part of the last cylinder because of retrace time. Lock in the sync to hold the patterns steady. The waveforms will follow the firing sequence of the engine; for example, on a 6-cylinder engine the first waveform on the left will be No. 1 cylinder, followed by Nos. 5, 3, 6, 2, and 4. This is called a "parade" pattern. Adjusting the sweep rate so that the patterns are piled on top of one another gives a "superimposed" pattern.

The individual waveforms in the parade pattern are quite small (on the typical service scope) and will not reveal much detail. The purpose of this pattern, though, is for quick comparison of the firing voltage and spark lines for each cylinder. The firing-voltage line is a high frequency component and may be rather dim. Because of the uncertainty of the divider ratio and frequency response of your pickup, this line may not be a true representation of actual firing voltage. However, comparative readings may still be made. These lines normally fluctuate but should be even within 25% of each other. For a typical engine, these lines represent about 5- to 8-thousand volts.

Likewise, the more or less horizontal spark lines should all be even with each other. These lines represent, for evaluation purposes, the amount of resistance in the secondary system. Excessive resistance will cause this line to be at a higher-than-normal voltage and of considerably shorter duration. Rather than having the idealized shape shown in Fig. 12-2, these lines tend to curve upward. As secondary resistance increases, this upward slope becomes more pronounced.

Having noted the spark and firing lines for each cylinder, you can now examine the intermediate and dwell sections. This examination is easier if you increase the horizontal gain, which spreads the patterns out for more detailed study. Examine the oscillations in the intermediate section; no oscillations mean a shorted coil. Remember, though, this section is a residual part of the overall waveform. High-speed or high-dwell angles may cause it to disappear. Next, examine the points-close signal at the beginning of the dwell section. It should normally be a short string of damped oscillations caused by the initial closing of the points. Erratic point action will frequently show up in this signal. Point arcing, on the other hand, will show up at the end of the dwell section, just before the start of the next firing line. This appears as a false start to the firing line and can be caused by excessive dwell or a faulty condenser.

Dwell angle, as observed on a scope, is the ratio of the dwell section length to the distance between two consecutive firing lines. Most commercial scopes have dwell scales imprinted on the graticule to show this ratio in terms of conventional dwell angle. The only advantage to measuring dwell in this manner is that individual cam-lobe dwells can be checked as a means of detecting cam wear. Conventional dwellmeters, of course, measure only the average dwell of all lobes. A simple method of comparing individual cam lobes, without actually measuring, is to use the superimposed pattern. Theoretically, each portion of the individual waveforms should be perfectly superimposed on one another. There is always a certain amount of dwell variation, but excessive variation is readily apparent.

If your scope and pickup were properly calibrated and compensated, you could measure available coil voltage. Even without this, you can get a relative indication of coil output. When a plug wire is lifted, coil voltage will rise to its maximum level (typically, 20-25 kilovolts) provided, of course, that there is no insulation breakdown. The waveform will look like that in Fig. 12-7A. The presence of breakdown causes the loss of a portion of the pattern, as shown in

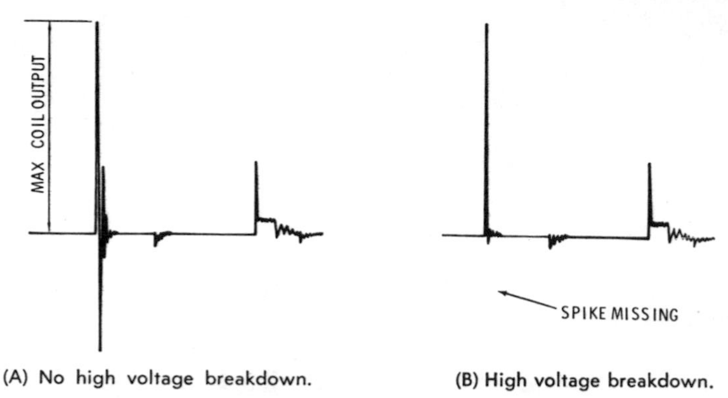

(A) No high voltage breakdown. (B) High voltage breakdown.

Fig. 12-7. Testing for coil output and voltage breakdown.

Fig. 12-7B. Notice in both examples that the firing lines (or what would have been the firing line in Fig. 12-7A) are almost at the same level. Only the absence of the opposite-going pulse in Fig. 12-7B distinguishes between normal and a case of high voltage breakdown. Notice how this test parallels the ignition tester described in Chapter 4.

Primary waveforms analysis is similar to secondary analysis and yields essentially the same information. Fig. 12-8 shows the normal primary waveform and its main elements. Except for the firing line, which is not truly reflected in the primary waveform, all equivalent information is available. Even the insulation breakdown test can be made with the primary pattern. The reader should compare, point for point, this pattern with the secondary pattern.

This comprises a basic ignition scope analysis. A scope has certain advantages; in particular, it is able to make a quick, overall check of the ignition system. On the other hand, it is not a "crystal ball"; it cannot see what is not there. It will detect fouled plugs (indicated by a marked drop in the firing and spark lines), but only if they short out at the time of testing. This will seldom happen during no-load tests in the shop, although it may under dynamometer testing.

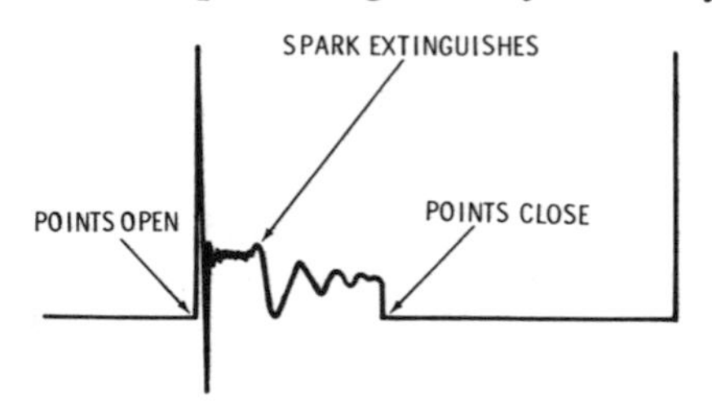

Fig. 12-8. The primary waveform.

13

Battery Testing

A few years ago the American Automobile Association made a survey on emergency road service calls. One of the most frequently cited reasons for service calls was battery trouble. One might draw from this conclusion that batteries are not too dependable. Nothing could be further from the truth. It shows, instead, how often batteries are neglected.

Neglect is one of the real causes of being caught with a dead battery. In spite of what people may tell you, batteries seldom die "all of a sudden." Their demise is usually a slow but unnoticed process. With just minimum attention and a little routine testing you should get all the life expectancy engineered into a battery—and probably even more. The purpose of this chapter is to describe various methods for detecting early signs of trouble, as well as other conditions that might lead to premature failure.

HOW BATTERIES WORK

To understand better how batteries are tested, we should know a little about how they are made, and in particular, how they function. The battery is completely chemical in operation. This can be shown by the following formula:

$$Pb + PbO_2 + 4H_3O^+ + 2SO_4^= \underset{\text{Charge}}{\overset{\text{Discharge}}{\rightleftharpoons}} 2PbSO_4 + 6H_2O$$

It is not necessary to be a chemist to see what the formula tells us. If a plate of lead, Pb (the negative plate, and a plate of lead dioxide (also called lead peroxide), PbO_2 (the positive plate) are immersed in an electrolyte solution of sulfuric acid (shown ionically as

$4H_3O^+ + 2SO_4^{=}$), and if the two plates are electrically connected to a load, a reaction occurs. The items on the left of the formula will be converted to those on the right. In the process, free electrons (current) will flow through the load. If the process is allowed to continue, both plates will be converted to lead sulfate, $PbSO_4$, and the electrolyte solution converted to water. At this point the battery is completely discharged. In actual practice, a battery would cease to function long before this point was reached.

The above process is reversible, also. If an opposing or charging current is passed through the two plates, the battery will be restored to its original condition. This, then, is the basic chemical operation of a lead-acid storage battery, or more specifically, one cell of a battery.

An automotive battery contains either three such cells (for a 6-volt battery) or six cells (for a 12-volt battery). Each cell contains a number of plates, depending on the electrical rating or capacity of the complete battery. The negative plates, molded of a lead alloy in a grid-like pattern, are filled with "spongy" lead. This is a porous form of lead that will present a large surface area to the electrolyte. The positive plates have a similar grid pattern but are filled with a lead-dioxide paste. The positive and negative plates are interleaved with nonconducting separators between each plate (Fig. 13-1). There is always one more negative plate than positive plate so that each positive plate will be sandwiched between two negative plates. Full utilization of the lead dioxide is thus assured.

The electrical capacity of the battery is determined primarily by the size and number of plates. A typical battery may have nine plates per cell—five negative and four positive plates. Since the electrical capacity or rating of a battery is important for test purposes, let's examine the various ways in which batteries are classed and rated.

BATTERY RATINGS

For size purposes only, batteries are given group numbers. These determine the physical dimensions of the battery but do not indicate its electrical capacity. This last factor is expressed in a variety of ways. Unless you are familiar with these methods, electrical ratings can be somewhat confusing.

The most common rating procedure is called the "20-hour method" and results in a specification known as the "amp-hr rating." The rating process works like this: a fresh, fully charged battery is discharged at a constant current selected so that at the end of 20 hours the individual cell voltage will have dropped from its normal 2.1 volts to 1.75 volts. This current multiplied by 20 hours equals the amp-hr rating of the battery. Thus, a discharge current of three amperes, for

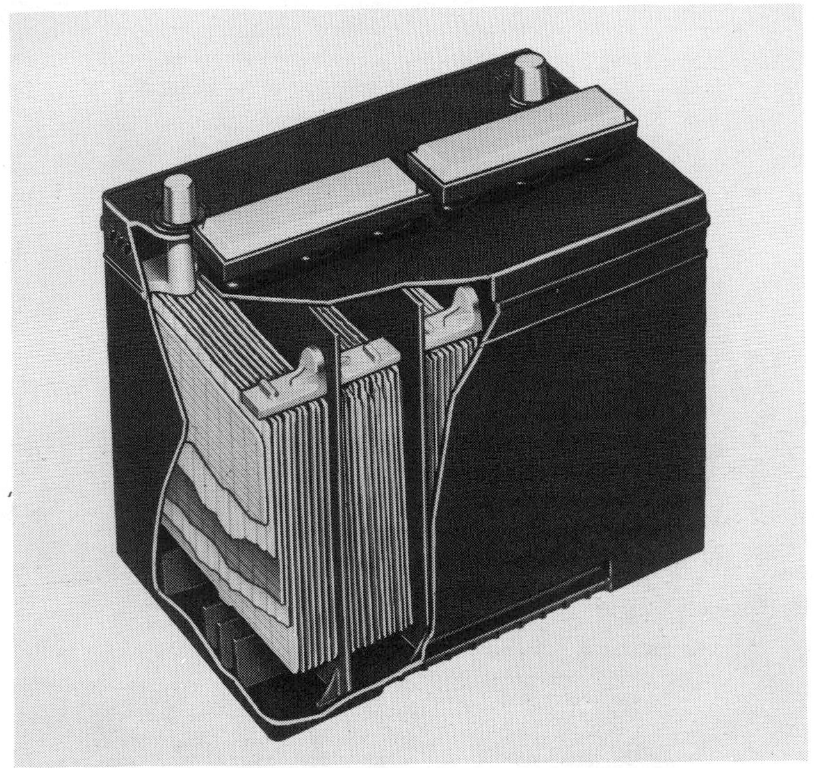

Courtesy Globe-Union Inc.

Fig. 13-1. Internal construction of a hard-top battery.

example, gives a 60 amp-hr rating. Contrary to common belief, this does not mean that 60 amperes can be drawn for one hour.

A battery rating frequently confused with the amp-hr designation is based on the "20-minute method" and gives a rating in amperes (not ampere-hours). This rating means that a battery at 80°F can be discharged at the rated current for 20 minutes before it drops to 1.5 volts per cell. This method is seldom used today.

Other methods of battery rating are also employed. The 0° cranking time, for instance, shows for how many minutes a battery at 0°F can deliver 150 amperes (300 amps for 6-volt batteries) before it drops to 1 volt per cell. Recently, two new methods have been introduced to show battery capacity in terms of its on-the-vehicle performance rather than under laboratory conditions. These are called "cold cranking performance" and "reserve capacity."

Cold cranking performance is measured at 0°F and shows how many amperes can be drawn from a battery for 30 seconds before it drops to 1.2 volts per cell. The reserve capacity is measured at 80°F and shows for how many minutes 25 amperes can be drawn from a battery before it drops to 1.75 volts per cell. This second rating indicates the approximate operating time of a car (with lights and heater) in the event of charging system failure. There is no direct correlation between amp-hr ratings and these two new methods, since the ratings are determined under different conditions. A given battery rated at 50 amp-hr may have a cold cranking performance of 305 amperes and a reserve capacity of 75 minutes. Another 50 amp-hr battery may have somewhat different specifications.

TEMPERATURE EFFECTS

An important factor seldom considered is the temperature efficiency of the battery. Since a battery is a chemical device, its output is proportional to its temperature. A battery that is considered to be 100% efficient at 80°F is only 40% efficient at 0°F (Fig. 13-2). At lower temperatures it is even less efficient. This assumes, of course, that the battery is initially healthy and fully charged. When making load tests on cold batteries, allowance should be made for their reduced efficiency at low temperatures.

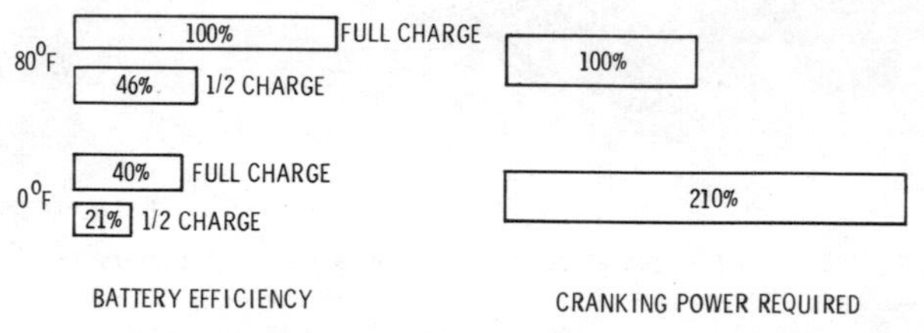

Fig. 13-2. Temperature effect on battery efficiency and cranking power.

THE BATTERY HYDROMETER

A variety of instruments have been designed for testing batteries. One of the most basic is the familiar battery hydrometer (Fig. 13-3). It will give you information about the battery that cannot be obtained by electrical test methods. For this reason, you should include, along with your other test instruments, a good quality, temperature-compensating hydrometer.

The hydrometer gives a direct measurement of a battery's specific gravity, which, in turn, is a direct indication of its state of charge. See Table 13-1. Many batteries, particularly 12-volt ones, have a full-charge specific gravity of 1.260. Others are fully charged at 1.275.

Hydrometers are calibrated to give the specific gravity at 80°F. A correction must be made for other battery temperatures. For every

10°F over 80°F, add .004 to the indicated reading; for every 10°F under 80°F, subtract this amount. The better hydrometers have a built-in thermometer that shows directly the proper correction.*

The actual use of the hydrometer requires no detailed explanation. Be sure that you take in just enough electrolyte to lift the float and keep it from sticking to the sides of the tube. If you take readings of a battery under charge, you may collect bubbles on the float. This can cause higher-than-normal readings. Record your readings to the nearest .005 specific gravity.

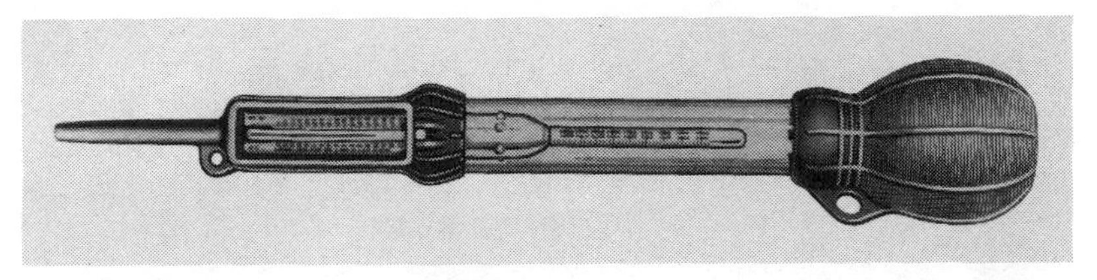

Courtesy E. Edelmann and Co.

Fig. 13-3. A temperature compensating hydrometer.

When battery testing with a hydrometer, the first thing to note is the overall state of charge. If it is not at full charge (1.260 to 1.275), make a point of finding out why. Something is wrong; sooner or later you may be faced with a "sudden" failure. The most usual causes of a partially discharged battery are:

1. Defective charging system. See Chapter 6.
2. Excessive electrical loads or an under-capacity charging system.
3. Unknown electrical drain, leakage or partial short.
4. Prolonged low speed driving with heavy electrical load.
5. Partially sulfated battery or loss of active material from the plates.

This last cause is due either to battery abuse or simply old age. If a battery is allowed to remain in a partially discharged condition for a period of time, the lead sulfate that normally forms on the plates during discharge will tend to harden. When this happens, it may not readily convert to acid during charging. As a result, the specific gravity, and hence the state of charge, cannot rise above a certain level, regardless of the amount of charging. This is why periodic checks (perhaps once a month) with a hydrometer are important to long battery life.

---

*A recently introduced hydrometer automatically compensates for temperature.

Table 13-1. State of Charge Versus Specific Gravity

Specific Gravity	State of Charge	Approximate Freezing Temperature
1.260 to 1.275	100%	—85° F
1.240 to 1.250	75%	—60° F
1.220 to 1.225	50%	—40° F
1.190 to 1.200	25%	—14° F
1.160	Discharged	+ 5° F

Another important hydrometer indication is the eveness of readings. Cell-to-cell variations in excess of .025 specific gravity indicate possible cell trouble. Variations in excess of .050 indicate almost certain cell failure. You may sometimes notice a dark or cloudy appearance of the electrolyte. This, too, points to impending cell trouble.

BATTERY LOAD TESTERS

Although the hydrometer shows the chemical condition of a battery, it does not directly indicate the electrical condition of the battery. To properly evaluate a battery requires that *both* these conditions be tested. The overall electrical performance of the battery is usually determined by what is called a "load test." This is also known as a "capacity test," "high rate discharge test," and, erroneously, as a "breakdown test." It simply involves applying a known, heavy load to the battery and measuring the resulting terminal voltage.

Garage-type battery load testers generally incorporate a variable carbon pile for applying the load. This permits the load to be adjusted to batteries of various capacities. The rule is that the load in amperes should equal three times the amp-hr rating of the battery. Thus a 50-amp-hr battery would be tested while under a 150-ampere load. To be considered good, the terminal voltage under this load should not fall below 9.6 volts (or 4.8 volts for 6-volt batteries). These are minimum acceptable voltages; a good battery will normally test somewhat higher.

A battery cannot be condemned on the basis of a load test alone unless its specific gravity is over 1.225. A battery that fails the load test and whose specific gravity is less than this may simply be in a discharged condition and not defective. The only way to be completely sure is to recharge it (which takes valuable time) and then retest. Usually, we want to know as quickly as possible whether a battery is worth saving. With the test circuits and methods to be described, you will be able to make a reasonably accurate evaluation of a battery in almost any state of charge.

A HOME-TYPE LOAD TESTER

Although most commercially built battery testers incorporate a loading device, the necessary materials for this are not readily available to the builder. A handy substitute, however, is the starter motor on the car. With a warm engine most starters draw approximately three times the recommended amp-hr rating of the battery. This is quite close to the proper testing load. The only hazard with this technique is that a defective starter may draw excessive current, thus over-testing the battery. The volt-amp tester described in Chapter 6 will quickly point out such a condition.

Since we will use the starter as a load, the battery load tester becomes nothing more than a 0–16-volt voltmeter with suitably marked test limits. Actually, almost any voltmeter could be used for this purpose. But because we will want to make additional tests, it is desirable to incorporate all the battery test functions in one specially designed instrument.

THE CELL BALANCE TEST

One of these additional functions is called a "cell balance test." Here is the theory behind it. When a load is applied, the terminal voltage of the battery will drop to some level. This voltage is the sum of the individual cell voltages, which, in a normal battery, should be equal to each other. A defective cell, when under load, will frequently show a few tenths of a volt less than the other cells. This may not be enough to be noticeable in the total terminal voltage. However, by comparing half of the cells in a battery against the other half, uneven cell voltages, no matter how slight, can be easily detected. The likelihood of compensating errors due to two equally bad cells is very remote.

Before the advent of hard-top batteries, this test was made simply by connecting a voltmeter to the center cell connector strap and, alternately, to the positive and negative battery posts. A load was applied, and the two voltage readings were compared to each other. A difference of 0.2 volt or more indicated cell trouble.

Hard-top batteries prevent a direct connection to the cell connector straps. Instead, the connection must be made chemically through the electrolyte solution. The best material for this purpose is cadmium. But cadmium rods, or even brass rods that are heavily plated with cadmium, are hard to come by. A convenient substitute that works reasonably well is common, 60/40 electrical solder. Regardless of the cell prod material, the circuit is the same. This is shown in Fig. 13-4. As you will notice, it is basically a bridge-type circuit.

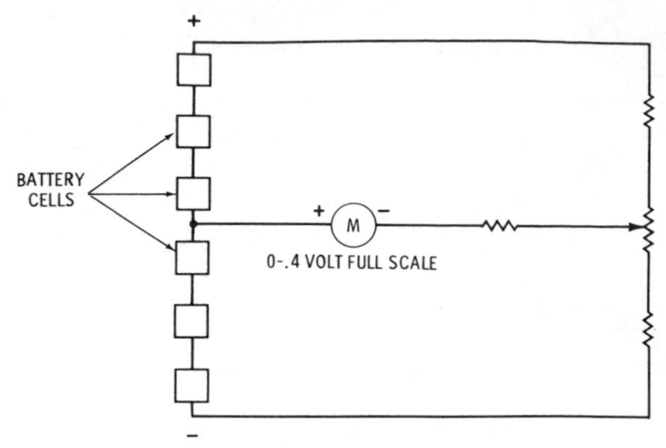

Fig. 13-4. The cell balance test circuit.

To use the circuit, the battery leads are connected to the battery posts and the cadmium (or solder) prod is inserted into the third cell from the positive post. The potential difference between the prod and the negative plates of this cell is on the order of 0.1 volt. This places the prod almost at the electrical center of the battery. The potentiometer is adjusted so the meter reads about ¾ full scale. The full range of the meter represents 0.4 volt. A cranking load is applied to the battery and the meter reaction is noted.

Normally, the meter reading will drop to about ½ or ¼ scale, indicating a voltage change, under load, of 0.1 to 0.2 volt. Most of this change is due to the decrease in potential between the negative plates and the cell prod that takes place under load and does not indicate cell variation. If the meter goes off scale, either to the right or left, an abnormal difference in cell voltages and cell condition is indicated. The load should be applied for at least 5 seconds, since even a weak cell can sometimes function normally for a short period.

THE CADMIUM TEST

Another battery test is called the "cadmium" or "cell voltage test." This is an old test, but one that did not become popular until the appearance of hard-top batteries. The original procedure was to insert a cadmium electrode into the cell electrolyte and measure the potential between first the positive and then the negative plates. Each cell was tested in this manner and the readings compared.

Because of the inaccessibility of the cell connector straps, this procedure has been modified. The present method is to use two cadmium prods inserted into the electrolyte of two adjacent cells. The resultant voltage is noted and the procedure repeated for each successive cell pairs. The voltage readings, for a normal battery, should not differ by more than .05 volt; a greater difference means possible cell trouble.

To measure these small differences in voltage, an expanded scale voltmeter is used. A simple way of doing this is shown in Fig. 13-5. This voltmeter gives a voltage range of 1.5 to 2.5 volts, or in other words, 1 volt for the full meter scale. Since 10% of the scale range represents 0.1 volt, it is easy to detect cell differences as small as .01 volt.

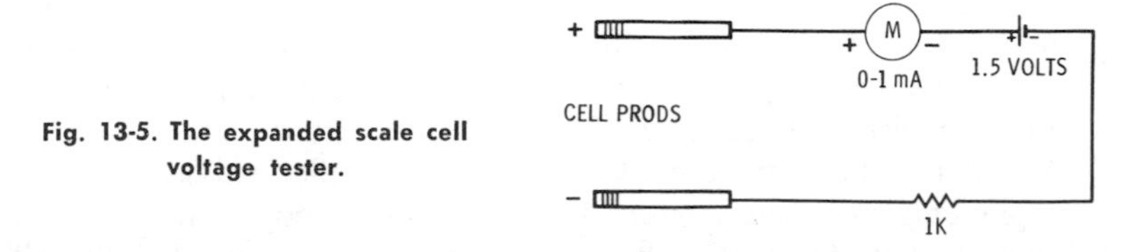

Fig. 13-5. The expanded scale cell voltage tester.

The proper prod material to use is cadmium. But again, a reasonable substitute can be found in solder. There is no specific way of making these prods; they serve merely to contact the electrolyte without touching the plates. One possible way of making a solder-type prod is shown in Fig. 13-6. A prod made of solder has a slight tendency to polarize, as shown by a gradual change in the meter reading. This can be prevented by slightly agitating the prods while taking a reading.

The cadmium-cell voltage test should not be made upon batteries recently on charge. When making the test on a car that has just been running, turn on the headlights for about one minute before beginning. Neither should this test be made on a battery that has just been subjected to a cranking load. Allow the battery to stabilize for several minutes before testing. Actually, with each voltage reading, you are testing part of one cell and part of another. But since it makes little difference *which* cell is failing, this causes no problem in testing. There are only five cell readings possible with this method (two read-

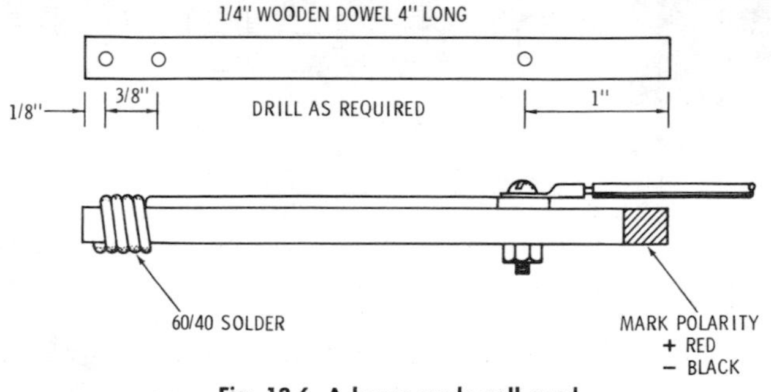

Fig. 13-6. A home-made cell prod.

ings with 6-volt batteries), although there are six cells. The cell closest to the positive terminal is tested with the negative prod in the cell hole and the other prod contacting the positive post. The voltage reading will be about .10-to .12-volt less than the other cell readings.

A MULTIFUNCTION BATTERY TESTER

Fig. 13-7 shows a circuit for a battery tester that incorporates all three of the previously discussed test functions. The only critical component is R1, the 15.6K 1% resistor for the 0–16-volt range. Since, the other two test ranges are primarily for comparative purposes, close tolerance resistors are not required.

A meter protection network, consisting of silicon diodes D1 and D2, prevents excessive current from flowing through the meter, regardless of how the test leads or prods may be connected. Since silicon diodes do not conduct until the impressed voltage is over 0.4 volt, they are effectively out of the circuit under normal conditions. However, if meter voltage should exceed that amount, they begin to conduct and clamp the voltage at a safe level.

The internal reference battery B1 for the cadmium cell test function can be any convenient size. The current drain is negligible. It should be fresh and have a terminal voltage of 1.50 to 1.55 volts. A test range for this battery is included so that it may be periodically checked. The 0–16-volt scale for the load test function can also serve

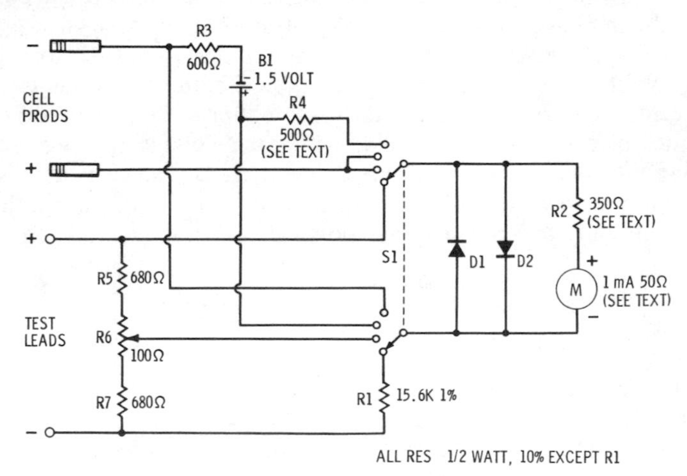

Fig. 13-7. A complete battery tester.

Table 13-2. Parts List for Battery Tester

Item	Description
B1	Battery, "C" cell, 1.5 volts
D1, D2	Diode, silicon, 50 volts, 200 mA or more
M	Meter, 0–1 mA, 50-ohms internal resistance
R1	Resistor, 15.6K, ½ watt, 1% (or hand-selected combination)
R2	See text
R3	Resistor, 600 ohms, ½ watt (hand selected)
R4	Resistor, 500 ohms, ½ watt (see text)
R5, R7	Resistor, 680 ohms, ½ watt, 10%
R6	Potentiometer, 100 ohms, wirewound, with shaft
S1	Switch, rotary, 2 pole, 4 position
Misc	18 ga twin conductor for battery leads and cell prod leads, large battery clips, battery holder for B1, case, and panel. See Fig. 13-6 for prod details.

as the checking scale for this reference battery. Select R4 to give a reading of 15 (equivalent to 1.5 volts) with a fresh cell. When the reading drops to 14 (1.4 volts), the reference battery should be replaced.

The resistor R2 should be so selected that its value plus the meter resistance equals 400 ohms. If the 1-milliamp meter has a 50-ohm armature, which is quite standard, 350 ohms will be needed. A series combination of 10% resistors is sufficiently accurate. Use large clips on the battery test leads because smaller clips can be sprung when forced over cable clamps. Also, rinse the cell prods in clear water after use. You may find it convenient to attach a small plastic bottle to the instrument for prod storage. See Table 13-2 for the battery tester parts list.

The Meter Dial

Although the various test readings could all be referred to the 0–16-volt scale, it is more convenient to use scales specifically drawn for each test function. (See Fig. 13-8.) The 0–16 scale is for the battery load test. The minimum acceptable voltage limits for this test are 9.6 volts for 12-volt batteries and 4.8 volts for 6-volt batteries. Since this scale is primarily for *go/no-go* purposes, it does not have to be finely graduated. The 1.5–2.5-volt range is for the cadmium-cell voltage test. This should be so scaled that you can detect a difference of .05 volt. The cell balance scale is simply a scale divided into four equal parts; each part equals 0.1 volt.

Testing With the Battery Tester

The general technique of using the various test functions has already been covered. However, the following is an overall battery

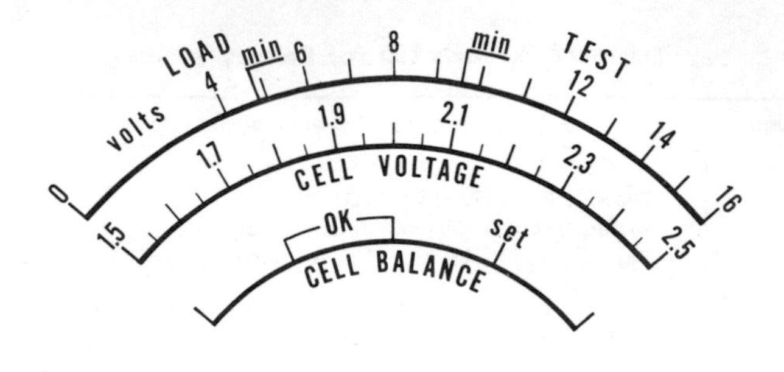

Fig. 13-8. A meter scale for the battery tester.

testing procedure, together with test interpretations, to provide a logical sequence of tests.

1. Visually examine battery, cables and clamps. Frequently a "dead" battery turns out to be a bad connection between a battery clamp and post. When faced with an apparently dead battery, an easy way to localize the trouble is to turn on the headlights and attempt to crank the engine. If the lights go out completely, the trouble is most likely in a clamp; if the lights dim considerably, the trouble is most likely a low battery.
2. Connect the battery tester leads to the battery posts and insert the positive prod in the third cell hole from the positive post. Set the test selector to the load test position, crank the engine for 5 seconds (pull the coil high tension wire to prevent starting), and note the voltage reading. Next, switch to the cell balance position, adjust meter to ¾-scale deflection, and crank engine for 5 seconds. Meter should drop to approximately ¼- or ½-scale deflection; other meter reactions indicate cell unbalance. (Note: If test leads are connected to the battery clamp rather than the post, a poor clamp-to-post connection can give the same indication as cell unbalance.)
3. If either of the above two tests show unsatisfactory results, further testing is required. Set the tester to the cell test position and turn on the headlights. Place the positive prod in the cell closest to the positive post and the other prod in the adjacent cell. Note the voltage reading. Transfer the prods to the next pair of cells, keeping the positive prod closest to the positive post. After noting the voltage reading, repeat this process for the remaining cell pairs. All readings should be within 0.5 volt. Test the positive cell by placing the positive prod in contact

with the positive post and the other prod in the cell hole. Add .10–.12 volt to this reading for comparative purposes.

4. When battery trouble is suspected, a specific gravity test should always be made. In fact, this test should be made routinely as an overall check on the performance of the charging system. By comparing gravity readings with the previous test results, you can make a more accurate analysis of battery condition.
   (a) Normal load and balance tests with low gravity generally indicate charging system trouble rather than battery trouble.
   (b) An otherwise good battery that is merely in a low state of charge (for example, below 1.225 specific gravity) may fail the load test. If the subsequent cell tests and specific gravity readings are even, recharging should restore the battery to normal condition. However, if the specific gravity does not rise to 1.260 or more after an adequate charge, the battery is either sulfated or has lost its capacity with age. If the specific gravity does not increase over a three-hour charge period (normal* 3–5 ampere slow charging), the battery has reached its maximum state of charge.
   (c) An excessive variation in cell voltage readings or more than a .05 variation in specific gravity readings almost invariably means potential cell failure. Depending on how far the trouble has progressed, it may or may not show up in the load or balance tests. The load and balance tests are quick, overall checks designed to detect imminent or existing battery problems; they cannot predict too far into the future. This is why periodic cell voltage and specific gravity readings are desirable.
   (d) An unsatisfactory reading during the balance test is almost certain evidence of imminent battery failure. Since a battery is like a chain, it takes only one bad cell to cause complete failure.

There is no guarantee that these procedures will catch every type of battery problem. However, if you follow this routine of periodic tests, it is rather unlikely that you will ever be caught by a "sudden" battery failure.

---

*Normal charge rate is equal to 1 amp per positive plate per cell.

14

Miscellaneous Testers

A LOW-RANGE OHMMETER

There are many times when troubleshooting involves resistance and continuity checks. It is not always practical to do this with the usual radio-tv service vom; the range of this instrument is not always low enough for automotive use. Most automotive electrical units are low resistance devices. Ballast resistors, for instance, are typically under 2 ohms; alternator field coils are about 4 to 5 ohms.

A practical automotive ohmmeter range has a 5-ohm midscale reading, which permits measuring to a fraction of an ohm. (Since most ohmmeters measure from zero to infinite resistance, the midscale reading is the standard method of specifying the useful range. The lowest midscale value of most voms is about 20 to 50 ohms.) To accomplish this without excessive drain on the tester battery requires a "back-up" or shunt-type ohmmeter. As the name implies, the scale reads backward from the usual ohmmeter scale. Fig. 14-1 shows such a circuit.

Resistor R1 is the critical component because it determines the overall accuracy of the instrument. Assuming that you are using a midscale reading of 5 ohms and a 50-ohm meter, R1 must equal 5.6 ohms. If you choose a different mid-scale value or have a different meter resistance, calculate R1 from the following formula:

$$R1 = \frac{R_s R_m}{R_m - R_s}$$

where,

R_s is the midscale reading,
R_m is the meter resistance.

The well-known warning that ohmmeters should never be used on "live" circuits is especially important here. Accidentally connecting the test leads to 12 volts can cause almost instant damage to R1 and the meter. Since this instrument is primarily for bench testing, such damage is unlikely. Attempting to fuse this circuit interferes with accuracy.

Calibrate the instrument by leaving the test leads open and adjusting R3 for full scale meter deflection (infinite resistance). When you clip the leads together, the meter may not drop completely to zero, due to the slight resistance in the leads and clips. For accurate measurements, this residual lead resistance should be noted and subtracted from the observed readings. In practice, however, such refinement is seldom necessary.

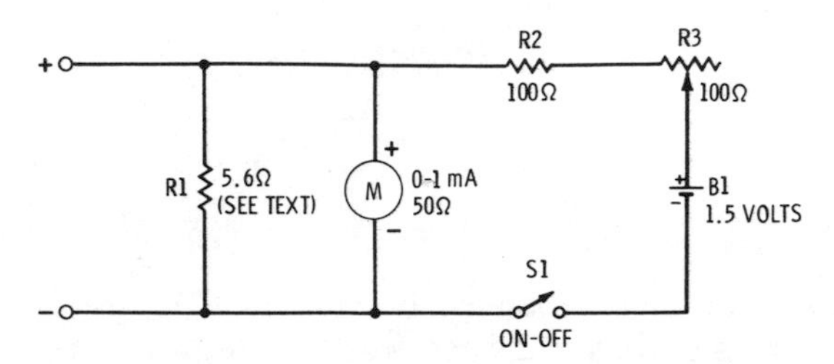

Fig. 14-1. A low-range automotive ohmmeter.

Another ohmmeter range that is especially useful in automotive work has a midscale reading of approximately 10K. This is used mostly for testing suppressor type (TVRS) spark plug wires. These wires are a frequent source of ignition trouble; when their resistance goes too high, they cause misfiring. Virtually all suppressor wires are under 30K; most are between 4K and 10K. Any resistance over 30K is considered excessive.

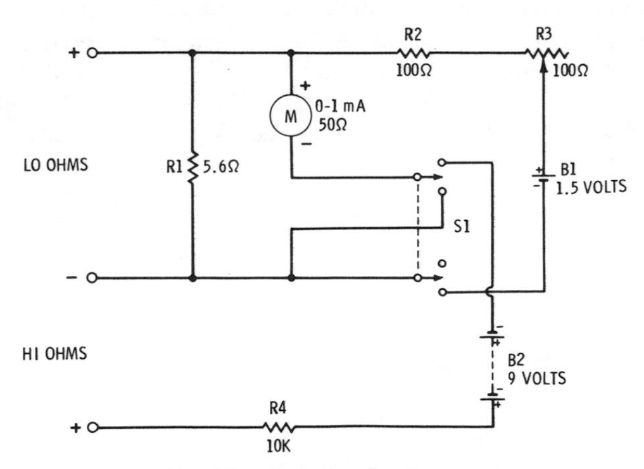

Fig. 14-2. A dual-range ohmmeter.

Only two additional parts are needed to add this high range (Fig. 14-2): a 9-volt transistor radio battery and a 10K resistor. You may have to alter this resistor somewhat to get a full-scale reading when the "high" leads are connected together. Because of its application, this range does not have to be accurately calibrated; it is primarily a go/no-go check. Use a center-off, dpdt toggle switch for the off-on and range switch. The three-lead arrangement was used in order to eliminate the switching of R1, because this might affect the low-range accuracy.

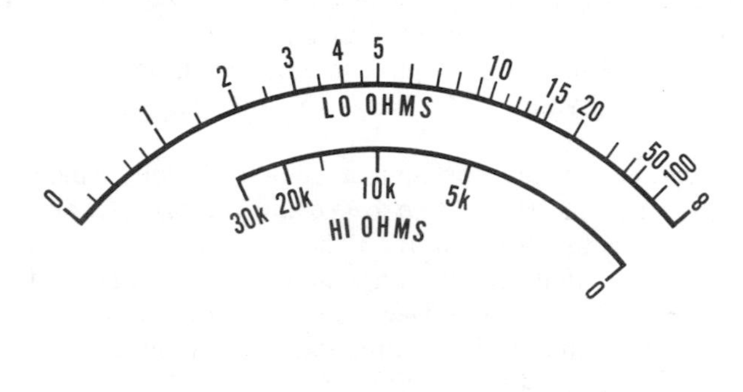

Fig. 14-3. The automotive ohmmeter dial.

Besides checking plug wires and suppressors, it can also be used to detect leakage in condensers, diodes, armatures and many other electrical devices. When testing diodes, though, remember that they must be disconnected from the stator windings to isolate the good from the bad. (The low range cannot be used for diode checks because the test voltage is too low.)

A typical meter scale that will fit most 3½-inch meters is shown in Fig. 14-3. For those who like to lay out their own dial, the major points can be calculated from these formulas:

a. Low Range $D = F.S. \frac{R_t}{R_t + R_s}$

b. High Range $D = F.S. \frac{R_s}{R_t + R_s}$

where,

D is the degrees of deflection,
F.S. is the full-scale degrees,
R_s is the midscale resistance,
R_t is the scale reading.

A SPECIAL VOLTMETER

As we have seen in the earlier chapters, voltmeters play an important role in automotive testing. Most testing and troubleshooting can be done with a simple 0–16-volt voltmeter. Sometimes, though, a specialized voltmeter can be even more helpful than the standard one.

One such instrument is the low range "voltage drop" meter. This is especially useful in tracking down intermittently loose connections. Such connections have the perversity of not acting up when we try to find them. One way of ferreting them out is to amplify their effect by using a very sensitive, low-range voltmeter.

A low-range voltmeter is simple enough; the important thing is to protect it from overvoltage. An easy way of doing this is shown in Fig. 14-4.

The basic range of this instrument is 0 to 1 volt, which permits variations as small as .01 volt to be readily detected. This range is controlled by resistors R1 and R2. The X2 switch inserts an additional 1K resistor, extending the range to 2 volts when needed. Diodes D1, D2, D3, and D4 are low-voltage silicon devices capable of handling 200 milliamperes. They function as overvoltage clamps, providing protection up to 15 volts or more. They will affect scale accuracy above 1.6 volts, but this is not serious. Normal voltage drops, depending on the circuit, usually range from .05 to 0.5 volt and, occasionally, up to 1 volt. The standard scale found on 0–1-mA meters will also serve as the 0–1-volt range.

A typical application for this instrument might be to find an intermittent connection in a headlight circuit. Connect the positive lead to the positive battery post. Connect the negative lead to the "hot" input of one of the head lamps. Turn on the headlights and note the voltage drop on the meter. This will normally be 0.5 to 1 volt, although abnormal resistance will cause it to be higher. Important to look for, though, is the steadiness of the reading. Intermittent connections show up as intermittent changes in the voltage drop, some-

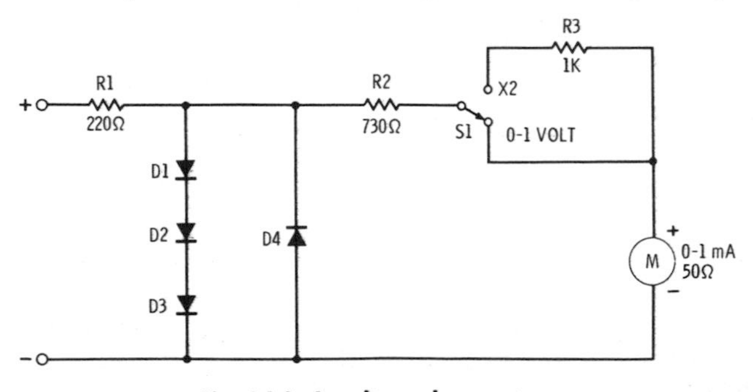

Fig. 14-4. A voltage drop meter.

times sending the meter off scale. By proding and tugging along the suspected circuit while watching the meter, you can usually localize the trouble spot. Remember that such troubles can also exist—and frequently do—in the ground circuits. For these, check voltage drop from the negative battery post to the unit ground. The voltage drop in ground circuits is normally less than 0.1 volt.

Other applications will suggest themselves. Because of the instrument's circuit protection, you can safely test such items as switches and solenoids. If you continue to get significantly different readings each time the switch is turned off and on, you may have a switch which is beginning to go bad.

AN IN-CIRCUIT DIODE TESTER

If the on-the-vehicle diode tester of Chapter 7 indicates a faulty alternator, it must be removed to pinpoint the trouble. The trouble could be in any one (or more) of the six diodes. The question is: Which one?

One approach is to test the forward and back resistance of each diode with an ohmmeter or test light. This method, however, requires that each diode be disconnected from the stator to isolate it from its neighbor. This can be time-consuming if they are soldered in.

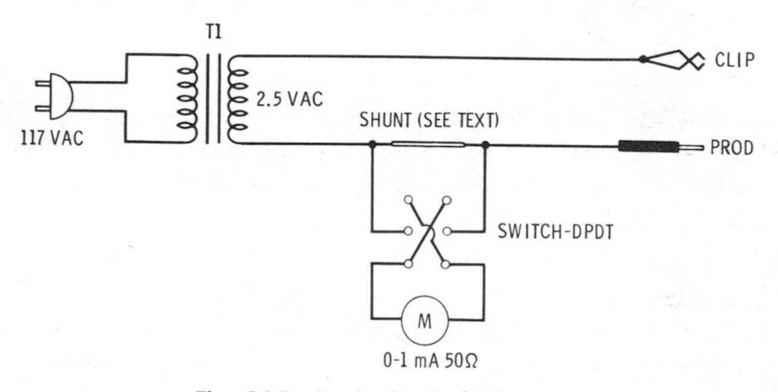

Fig. 14-5. An in-circuit diode tester.

The diodes can be effectively isolated without disconnecting by the normal inductive reactance of the stator windings. We can take advantage of this by using an ac ohmmeter instead of the usual dc ohmmeter. Such circuits are quite simple, as shown in Fig. 14-5.

The trick is to use a low-voltage transformer, such as a 2.5-volt filament transformer rated at about 2 amperes. Circuit resistance should be kept to a minimum. The meter can be either a 3–5-amp dc unit or a 0–1-milliamp type. A 0–1-milliamp meter with a 40–50-ohm internal resistance can be shunted down with about 6–8 inches of 24-gauge wire (use longer wire if internal resistance is higher). A

Fig. 14-6. A typical press-in diode.

Courtesy C. E. Niehoff and Co.

normal test reading is about ¾ full scale, using any convenient reference scale. Adjust the shunt if necessary. The meter reversing switch is needed to test both positive and negative case diodes.

The test is primarily comparative. After opening the suspected alternator, clip one test lead to the output terminal. (Note: Motorola alternators have an extra isolation diode(s) in series with the output terminal. On these alternators, clip the test lead to the "auxiliary" terminal. Test the isolation diode separately.) Firmly touch the test prod to each of the three diode pigtail leads and note the relative meter readings. A faulty diode will read about 10% or more below a good diode. This test sequence checks the three diodes in the positive cluster.

Next, reconnect the test clip to the alternator frame. Reverse the meter switch. Again touch the test prod to each of the three diode pigtail leads and note the relative meter readings. Even though it appears that you are touching the same three connections as above, you are actually testing the three diodes in the negative cluster.

A shorted diode will cause a zero reading. Since the stator windings do not provide complete isolation, this shorted diode will lower the readings considerably on the other two diodes, even though they may be good. Replacing the faulty diode should restore all readings to normal. An open diode will register about 10% to 20% lower than a good diode.

Replacing a bad diode is not too difficult. Some alternators have soldered or welded diode assemblies (three diodes per assembly) that must be replaced in sets. Others, though, use pressed-in diodes (Fig. 14-6) that can be replaced individually. Removing and replacing these devices can be done with a large "C" clamp and a few pieces of short tubing. Examination of the unit will quickly reveal the best way of doing this.

A word of caution on replacing diodes. Diodes come in two polarities: positive case and negative case. Be sure to specify not only

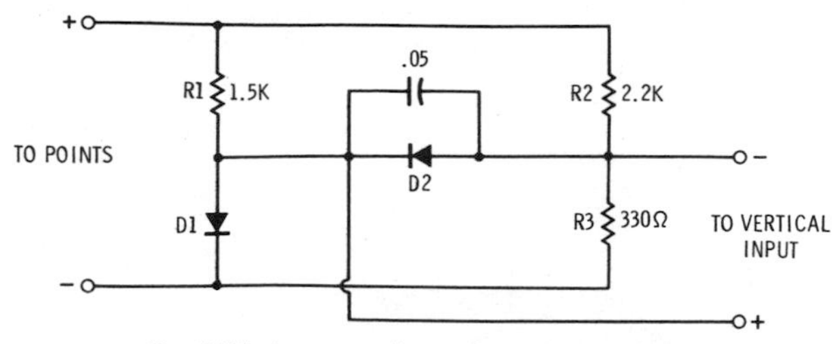

Fig. 14-7. A scope adapter for points testing.

the type of alternator, but whether you want a diode for the positive cluster (the one connected to the output terminal) or the negative cluster (the grounded one). Double check to make sure the new diode tests in same polarity as the other diodes in the cluster.

A SCOPE ADAPTER FOR TESTING POINTS

By slightly modifying the dynamic point resistance test circuit of Chapter 3, you can adapt it for scope testing. This is shown in Fig. 14-7.

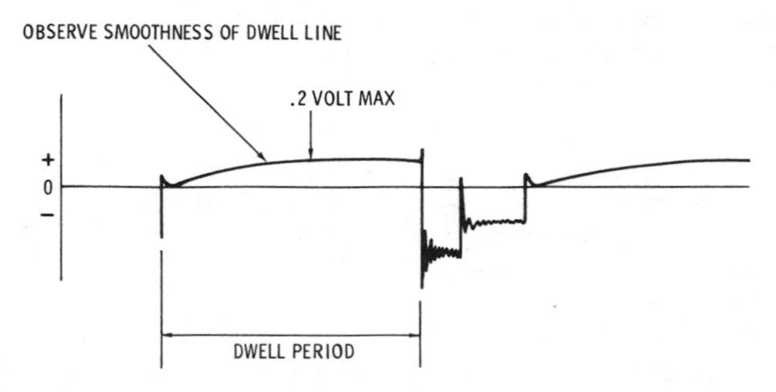

Fig. 14-8. Waveform observed with the points testing scope adapter.

The circuit will work on almost any type of scope. It has the advantage of greatly magnifying breaker point action and condition over what is normally seen in the primary or secondary waveforms. Fig. 14-8 shows the typical waveform for normal points. The important part of this pattern is the dwell period, which should be smooth and not greatly exceed .15 volt.

15

Construction Hints

Whether you are an old hand or just getting started in electronic construction, you may find here a number of useful tips that can save you both time and money. And saving you money is one of the aims of this book. This chapter is divided into two sections: (1) components and (2) construction. In the first section, we will discuss what kinds of parts to buy, how to use "junk box" parts, and how to substitute parts. In the second section we will cover various ways of making circuit boards.

COMPONENTS

Resistors

In general, three factors must be known in specifying a resistor: (1) ohmic value, (2) resistance tolerance, and (3) wattage rating. Unless otherwise specified, the resistors used in the foregoing projects are standard ½ watt, 10% tolerance devices. The required ohmic values are shown in the schematics and parts lists. Unless you wish to experiment, use the values shown. If necessary, you can obtain a particular value by combining two or more resistors in series or parallel. See Fig. 15-1.

In a few instances you will need high wattage resistors. It is permissible to go higher in wattage but never lower. You can frequently get the proper wattage by combining two lower wattage resistors either in series or parallel, providing you get the desired ohmic resistance. Calculating the combined wattage value can be a bit tricky if the ohmic resistances are unequal. However, if the individual wattage and resistance values are equal, the total wattage will be the sum of the individual wattages. For examples, a 2-ohm, 10-watt resistor can be made from two 1-ohm, 5-watt resistors wired in series. It can also be made from two 4-ohm, 5-watt resistors wired in parallel.

Precision, 1% resistors are usually specified for voltmeter circuits. If the specified value is used, they virtually eliminate any calibration. In single-lot purchases, though, they can be rather expensive. You can achieve the same results by hand-selecting 10% tolerance resistors and combining them to get the desired value. Pick a 10% unit whose

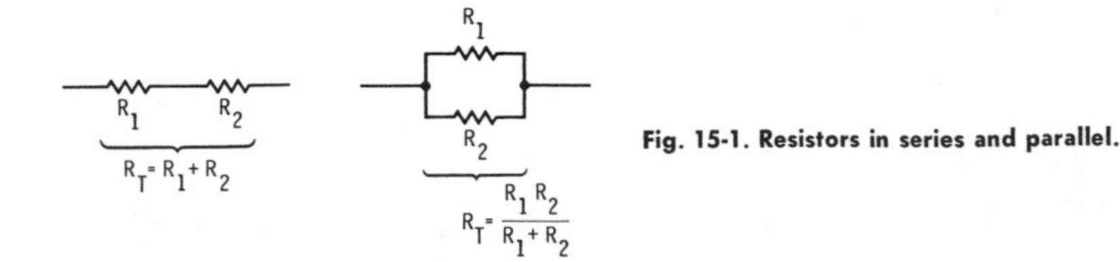

Fig. 15-1. Resistors in series and parallel.

ohmic value is just under the specified value. Then add, in series, a low value 10% resistor as a "trimmer." By having your voltmeter connected to a known voltage source, you will know when you have selected the correct trimmer. (See Chapter 6.)

Capacitors

There are three types of capacitors used in the previous circuits: (1) paper or mylar film, (2) tantalums, and (3) electrolytics. These, like resistors, are also specified by three factors: capacitance, tolerance, and voltage rating. The capacitance shown in the schematics and parts lists is given in microfarads (μF). In general, capacitance should be within $\pm$20% of the specified value. You may use a higher voltage rating, but it is not recommended to use a lower one.

The charging capacitors used in tach circuits are tantalum types and should have a tolerance of $\pm$ 10% or better. An under-capacitance unit can be increased by paralleling with a small value "trimmer" capacitor. Tantalum capacitors, unlike paper or mylar film capacitors, are polarized. That is, they have a plus and a minus end and must be installed properly in the circuit. This polarity is shown on the circuit boards by a small plus sign.

Electrolytic capacitors are also polarized and must be properly installed. This polarity, too, is shown on the circuit boards. The capacitance tolerance on electrolytics is not critical; stock tolerances are adequate.

Capacitors vary in physical size, even though they may have comparable electrical ratings. For printed-circuit applications, you will want the smaller sizes, so check dimensions before ordering. Mylar capacitors are usually smaller than paper capacitors. Tantalums are always small and present no mounting problems.

Diodes

Three types of diodes are used in the various projects. The zener diode is a voltage regulating device specified by its zener voltage and wattage rating. A one-watt rating is adequate for all the listed circuits. Since these diodes are usually used in tach circuits, their voltage rating is important. If you cannot get the specified value, use the closest higher value. This will cause a slightly higher-than-normal meter deflection, but it can easily be calibrated out. On the other hand, low voltage may not sufficiently drive the meter.

The second group, the silicon diodes, are specified primarily by their voltage rating. Technically, this is known as the "peak inverse voltage" rating, (*piv*). As with other components, you can use a high

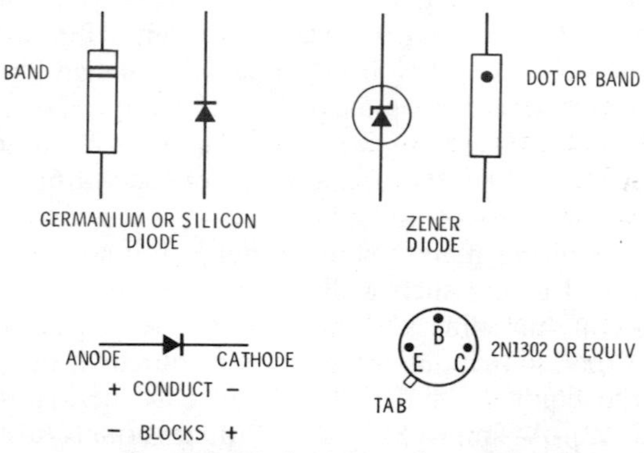

Fig. 15-2. Diode and transistor polarity.

voltage rating, but it is not recommended to use a lower rating. For instance, if the circuit calls for a 50-volt silicon diode, you could use a 100-or even a 400-volt unit. The forward conduction characteristic of silicon diodes, which is our main concern, is essentially independent of *piv* rating. Any silicon diode capable of handling 500 milliamps forward current can be used.

Germanium diodes make up the third group. For this application, the general-purpose 1N34 type is specified. However, any germanium diode having similar characteristics can be used.

All diodes must be installed in proper polarity. The cathode end is frequently indicated by a band. See Fig. 15-2.

Meters

All circuit projects are designed to use a 0–1 milliamp meter with 50 ohms of internal resistance. This is an economical and readily available type and is quite common in the surplus market. The internal resistance of a meter can be checked with a service type vom (use the R × 10 range to avoid excessive ohmmeter current). If the resistance is less than 50 ohms, you can either leave it as is or add resistance to bring it up to 50 ohms. If it is over 50 ohms, you may have difficulty calibrating the ammeter circuits, although it will usually work satisfactorily in the other circuits. You can compensate by making the ammeter shunt slightly longer.

Most meters have a scale deflection angle of either 90 or 100 degrees. The scale for the Master Analyzer is laid out for a 4½-inch meter with 90-degree deflection. All of the other meter dials are laid out for 3½-inch meters with 100-degree deflections. This was based on the most prevalent practices for the sizes involved. However, almost any meter can be adjusted to deflect between 90 and 100 degrees by shifting the lower hairspring arm. Depending upon whether you increase or decrease the original deflection angle, you will also increase or decrease the original full-scale sensitivity. For instance, increasing a 90-degree meter to 100 degrees will change its sensitivity from 1.0 milliamp to approximately 1.1 milliamps. Normally, this presents no problem except for voltmeter circuits. In these cases, it will be necessary to reduce the ohmic value of the voltmeter resistors by about 10%.

All projects requiring meters show either a full-size meter dial or the directions for drawing such a dial. The full-size dials can be reproduced on a copy machine and pasted over the original meter dial, or you can use them as guides in laying out your own design. If you like, add a little color to the dial with a self-adhering transparent film known as Zip-A-Tone. This and similar brands are available from art supply stores.

Some meters, such as those made by API (Assembly Products, Inc.), incorporate readily removable scales. Such a feature allows you to switch the meter from one circuit to another and still retain a custom look. This is a cost advantage for the lesser used instruments. With a little ingenuity, many standard meters can also be modified for changeable scales.

Chokes

The required chokes are not critical components. You can purchase the type specified in the parts lists (or an equivalent one) or make your own. If you wind your own chokes, you can make almost a dozen for the price of a factory wound one. Use 37-gauge enamel insulated magnet wire. The coil form or bobbin can be made of thin cardboard as shown in Fig. 15-3. If the wire is heavily insulated, you may have to increase the size of the bobbin to get the required resistance. When the bobbin is filled with wire, the resistance should be approximately 200 ohms. Use a brass or plastic screw for mounting the choke.

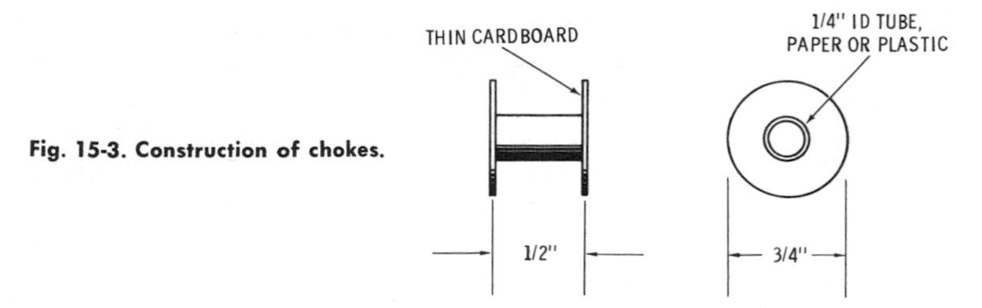

Fig. 15-3. Construction of chokes.

Transistors

The transistors used in these circuits are essentially switching devices. The specified 2N1302 or equivalent works well. Since the circuits have been designed for germanium transistors, do not substitute silicon devices. See Fig. 15-2 for lead identification.

Switches

Both rotary- and toggle-action switches are used. Slide switches may be substituted for toggle switches if desired. Use only rotary switches described as "nonshorting" types.

CONSTRUCTION

Hand Wiring

All of the circuits described in this book are simple enough to be made with hand-wiring techniques. If you plan to make the complete Master Analyzer, though, it is recommended that you use printed-circuit boards. A number of hand-wiring methods are available to the builder, from simple terminal strip mounting to prepunched circuit boards. Hand-wired circuits have the advantage of easy modification, which is important if you are doing experimental work. Once you have decided upon the final circuit, you may wish to convert it to printed-circuit construction.

Printed-Circuit Construction

Whether you use the prepared patterns shown in the earlier chapters or draw your own, the methods of producing a printed-circuit board are the same. Two approaches are commonly used: (1) the photographic method and (2) the "direct" method. We will discuss both techniques and let you decide which is best for your purposes.

The Photographic Method—The photographic method provides the greatest accuracy and the finest reproduction of detail. Although this may be important for certain commercial or industrial applications, it is not a requirement for the circuits shown in this book. For the builder the advantages of the photographic method (Fig. 15-4) are that he can readily duplicate the same board and that little actual labor is involved. The disadvantage is the cost of materials.

To use this method you will need:

1. Photosensitized copper clad board.
2. Developer.
3. Etchant.
4. A negative of the printed-circuit pattern.

The first three items can be bought in small quantities from electronic supply houses. The 1-oz grade (.00135″ foil thickness) of copper-clad on a XXXP paper base is sufficient. The negative can be obtained from a photographer, or your own facilities. If you are using the prepared patterns in the book, use a full-size negative.

In addition, you will need a yellow "bug" light or low wattage standard bulb, a No. 2 photoflood lamp, a sheet of glass, and a shallow developing tray. Work under subdued or yellow light until developing is completed. The manufacturer gives specific directions for exposing the sensitized board, but the general procedure is:

1. Place the negative on top of the sensitized surface of the printed-circuit board (be sure it is right side up).
2. Place the glass sheet on top to ensure intimate contact between negative and board.
3. Suspend photoflood lamp the specified distance above board and expose for the required time.
4. After exposing, place board in developer and agitate for the prescribed time.

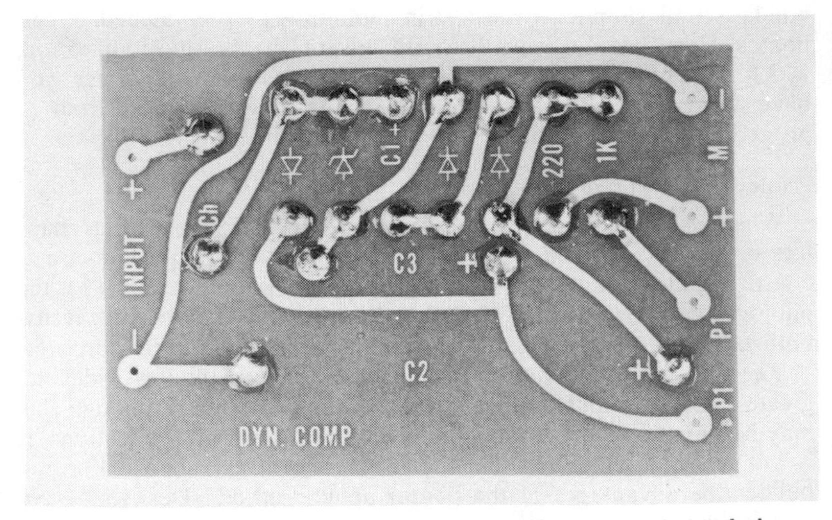

Fig. 15-4. A printed-circuit board constructed by the photographic method.

After developing, the board may be taken into ordinary room light for etching. The developer itself (frequently trichloroethylene) is not light-sensitive, but it evaporates quickly if left uncovered.

The etchant is usually a ferric chloride solution. A pint of commercially prepared solution will handle all the boards illustrated in this book. Pour the etchant into a shallow glass or plastic tray large enough to hold the circuit board. The board must be completely submerged. The secret of quick etching is agitation. Gently rock the tray to keep the solution moving. Periodically inspect the progress of the etching. A light pink color shows that the copper is being etched away. When all of the unwanted copper has been dissolved, remove the board and wash in clear water. It is now ready for drilling.

The mounting holes for most of the components should be .04 inch in diameter (use a No. 60 drill). The holes for adjusting potentiometers and similar parts should be just large enough to admit the terminals. After drilling, remove all burrs and the photoresist film by rubbing with fine steel wool. If the resist is not removed, the board will not solder. This completes the circuit board.

When mounting the components to the board, be sure to observe polarity, if indicated. This applies to tantalum and electrolytic capacitors and to all diodes. Bend the leads slightly to keep the components from falling out prior to soldering.

Printed-circuit board soldering is a technique that can be learned only by practice. Use a small point, low wattage soldering iron (40–60 watts) and 60/40 resin core solder. Be sure the iron is well tinned. Bring the iron and solder to the connection point at the same time, leaving the iron on just long enough for the solder to flow out. If the solder does not flow out but remains "balled up," you have what is known as a cold solder connection—and possibly future trouble. If the copper foil is overheated, it may lift away from the board.

A skilled technician can solder quickly enough to avoid overheating delicate components such as diodes and transistors. A safer approach, though, is to place small heat sink clamps or needle nose pliers on the leads before soldering. These absorb the heat that runs up the lead and prevent it from entering the component. After soldering, trim excess leads and check for solder "bridges" that may cause shorts.

The Direct Method—This technique requires more work but is quite economical. Several approaches are possible, depending on the materials available. For this method you will need:

1. Unsensitized copper clad board (1 ounce grade).
2. Full-size copy of pattern.
3. Carbon paper.
4. Lacquer resist (or model airplane dope) or adhesive-backed contact paper.

The first step is to thoroughly clean the copper clad board with fine steel wool. If all surface oxidation is not removed, the copper may not etch. Lay the carbon paper on the board and place the pattern copy on top. Using a sharp pencil, trace the circuit, pressing hard enough to transfer the image to the copper. With lacquer and a fine brush, fill in the areas for the conductors. Let dry, then etch as described above. Remove the lacquer resist with suitable solvent or steel wool. Center punch the hole locations and drill in the normal manner.

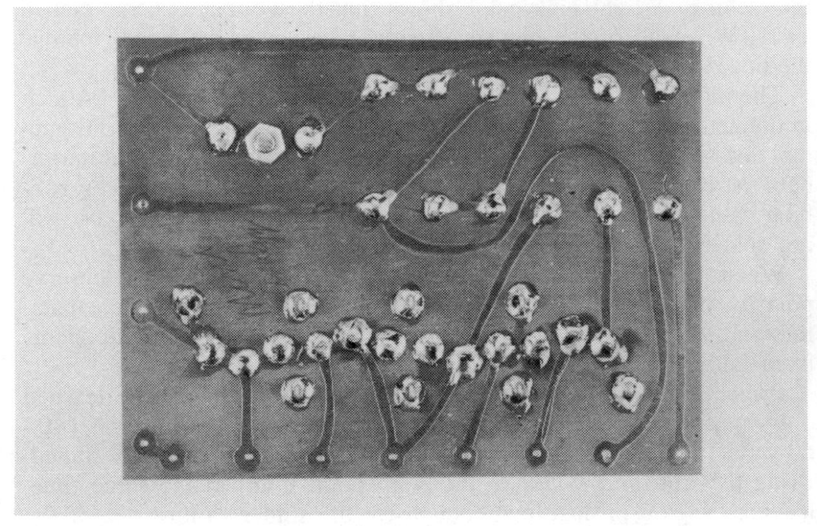

Fig. 15-5. A printed-circuit board constructed by the direct method.

Instead of lacquer, you can use a resist made of adhesive-backed contact paper. This inexpensive material is sold in hardware stores for decorative covering. A plain white or yellow works best. After cleaning the copper with steel wool, cover the surface with contact paper. Place the carbon paper on the contact paper and then the pattern copy. Transfer the circuit by tracing with a hard pencil. Using a fine-pointed modelmakers knife (or frisket knife), cut through the contact paper, following the circuit pattern. Keep the blade sharp by honing on fine emery paper. Peel off the paper covering the areas to be etched and rub down the remaining paper. Etch as previously described. Remove the remaining paper and mark for drilling.

The direct method, of course, does not give the "professional" look that the photographic method gives (Fig. 15-5), but the finished circuit boards function just as well. There are a number of other techniques for making printed-circuit boards described in electronic catalogs and books dealing with this subject.